A Cavendish Quantum Mechanics Primer

M. Warner & A. C. H. Cheung
University of Cambridge

Periphyseos Press

PERIPHYSEOS PRESS
Cambridge

Cavendish Laboratory
J. J. Thomson Avenue, Cambridge CB3 0HE, UK

Published in the United Kingdom by Periphyseos Press, Cambridge
www.periphyseos.org.uk

Information on this title is available at: www.cavendish-quantum.org.uk

First published 2012

Printed in the United Kingdom at the University Press, Cambridge

Typeset by the authors in LaTeX

A catalogue record for this publication is available from the British Library

ISBN 978-0-9572873-0-3 Paperback

Contents

PREFACE

This primer, starting with a platform of school mathematics, treats quantum mechanics "properly". You will calculate deep and mysterious effects for yourself. It is decidedly not a layman's account that describes quantum mechanical phenomena qualitatively, explaining them by analogy where all attempts at analogy must fail. Nor is it an exhaustive textbook; rather this brief student guide explains the fundamental principles of quantum mechanics by solving phenomena such as how quantum particles penetrate classically forbidden regions of space, how particle motion is quantised, how particles interfere as waves, and many other completely non-intuitive effects that underpin the quantum world. The mathematics needed is mostly covered in the AS (penultimate) year at school. So take heart! The quantum mechanics you will see may look formidable, but it is all accessible with your existing skills and with practice.

Chapters 1–3 require differentiation, integration, trigonometry and the solution of two types of differential equations met at school. The only special function that arises is the exponential, which is also at the core of school mathematics. We revise this material. In these chapters we cover quantisation, confinement to potential wells, penetration into forbidden regions, localisation energy, atoms, relativistic pair production, and the fundamental lengths of physics. Exercises appear throughout the notes. It is vital to solve them as you proceed. They will make physics an active subject for you, rather than the passive knowledge gained from popular science books. Such problem solving will transform your fluency and competence in all of the mathematics and physics you study at school and the first years at university. Especially, the gained confidence in mathematics will underpin further studies in any science; in any event, mathematics is the natural language of physics.

Chapter 4 needs complex numbers. It introduces the imaginary number $i = \sqrt{-1}$, something often done in the last year at school. Armed with i, you will see that quantum mechanics is essentially complex, that is, it involves both real and imaginary numbers. Waves, so central to quantum mechanics, also require revision. We shall then deal with free particles and their currents, reflection from and penetration of steps and barriers, flow of electrons along nano-wires and related problems. Calculating these phenomena precisely will consolidate your feeling for i, and for the complex exponentials that arise, or introduce you first to the ideas and practice in advance, if you are reading them a few months early. Finally, Chapter 5 introduces partial derivatives which are not generally done at school, but which are central to the whole of physics. They are a modest generalisation of ordinary derivatives to many variables. Chapter 5 opens the way to quantum dynamics and to quantum problems in higher dimensions. We revisit quantum dots and nano wires more quantitatively. Chapters 4 and 5 are more advanced and will take you well into a second-year university quantum mechanics course.

Some readers will find Chapters 4 and 5 challenging at first. Physics is an intellectually deep and difficult subject, wherein rests its attraction to the ambitious student. While moving from exposure-level treatments to the real edifice of physics, think of Alexander Pope

> A little learning is a dangerous thing;
> drink deep, or taste not the Pierian spring:
> there shallow draughts intoxicate the brain,
> and drinking largely sobers us again.

Alexander Pope (1688–1744)
from "An Essay on Criticism", 1709

Physics is a linear subject; you will need the building blocks of mechanics and mathematics to advance to quantum mechanics, statistical mechanics, electromagnetism, fluid mechanics, relativity, high energy physics and cosmology. This book takes serious steps along this path of university physics. Towards the end of school, you already have the techniques needed to start this journey; their practice here will help you in much of your higher mathematics and physics. We hope you enjoy a concluding exercise, quantising the string — a first step towards quantum electrodynamics.

Mark Warner & Anson Cheung
Cavendish Laboratory, University of Cambridge.
June, 2012

ACKNOWLEDGEMENTS

We owe a large debt to Robin Hughes, with whom we have extensively discussed this book. Robin has read the text very closely, making great improvements to both the content and its presentation. He suggested much of the challenging physics preparation of chapter 1. Robin and Peter Sammut have been close colleagues in The Senior Physics Challenge, from which this primer has evolved. Peter too made very helpful suggestions and was also most encouraging over several months. Both delivered some quantum mechanics to advanced classes in their schools, using our text. We would be lost without their generosity and without their deep knowledge of both physics and of school students. Peter also shaped ACHC's early physics experiences.

Quantum mechanics is a counter-intuitive subject and we would like to thank Professor David Khmelnitskii for stimulating discussions and for clarification of confusions; MW also acknowledges similar discussions with Professor J.M.F. Gunn, Birmingham University. We are most grateful to Dr Michael Rutter for his indispensible computing expertise. Dr Dave Green has been invaluable in his support of our pedagogical aims with the SPC and this book, where he has assisted in clarifying our exposition. We also thank colleagues and students who read our notes critically: Dr Michael Sutherland, Dr Michael Rutter; Georgina Scarles and Avrish Gooranah. Generations of our departmental colleagues have refined many of the problems we have drawn upon in this primer. We mention particularly the work of Professor Bryan Webber. Of course, any slips in our new problems are purely our responsibility.

ACHC thanks Trinity College for his Fellowship.

The Ogden Trust was a major benefactor of the SPC over many years of the project. The wider provision of these kinds of notes for able and ambitious school students is one of our goals that has been generously supported by the Trust throughout.

TEACHING RESOURCES

This primer grew from lecture notes written for the Senior Physics Challenge (SPC), the schools physics development project of the Cavendish Laboratory, University of Cambridge. We aim to make it as widely available as possible to school and university students alike: chapter 1 can be seen as a resource of problems and as an assembly of skills needed for Oxbridge entry tests and interviews. The coincidence of this function with that of preparing for university level quantum mechanics is not accidental — fluency and confidence in its material is also needed for continuing study. Practice over a period will be required for the mastery of chapter 1, but the material is not advanced. It is then required for the remainder of the book and in all higher physics. Chapters 2 and 3 would offer further practice for fluency while exploring the wonders of quantum mechanics. Chapters 2–5 form the core of our first two years of quantum mechanics teaching in Cambridge.

Chapter 1 is freely downloadable at this primer's website[1] and at the Senior Physics Challenge website[2].

Please consult THE PERIPHYSEOS PRESS[3] for *very* substantial price reductions for group or bulk orders of this primer.

THE PERIPHYSEOS PRESS derives its name from Greek "peri" = "about, concerning", and "physeos" = "(of) nature" — the same root as physics itself. The Press aims to make texts on natural sciences easily and cheaply available to students. The crocodile symbol (© M.J. Rutter), commissioned for the Cavendish Laboratory by the great Russian physicist Kapitza, is thought to be a reference to Lord Rutherford, the then Cavendish Professor.

AN INSTRUCTOR'S MANUAL[2] is available to teachers as a companion to the primer. It has full solutions to all the problems of the text and solved problems that go beyond the text itself. Points of difficulty, subtlety and extension are also discussed in the manual.

We would be grateful for suggestions for further material, or being made aware of typographical and other errors that readers might find in the text. Please contact us via the Primer's website.

---

[1] www.cavendish-quantum.org.uk
[2] www-spc.phy.cam.ac.uk
[3] www.periphyseos.org.uk

Mathematical symbols and notation; Physical quantities

Greek symbols with a few capital forms (alphabetical order is left to right, then top to bottom):

α	alpha	β	beta	$\gamma\ \Gamma$	gamma	$\delta\ \Delta$	delta	ϵ	epsilon
ζ	zeta	η	eta	$\theta\ \Theta$	theta	ι	iota	κ	kappa
λ	lambda	μ	mu	ν	nu	$\xi\ \Xi$	xi	o	omicron
$\pi\ \Pi$	pi	ρ	rho	$\sigma\ \Sigma$	sigma	τ	tau	$\upsilon\ Y$	upsilon
$\phi\ \Phi$	phi	χ	chi	$\psi\ \Psi$	psi	$\omega\ \Omega$	omega	∇	nabla

Miscellaneous symbols and notation:

For (real) numbers a and b with $a < b$, the *open* interval (a,b) is the set of (real) numbers satisfying $a < x < b$. The corresponding *closed* interval is denoted $[a,b]$, that is, $a \leq x \leq b$.

$\in$ means "in" or "belonging to", for example, the values of $x \in (a,b)$.

$\sim$ means "of the general order of" and "having the functional dependence of", for instance $f(x,y) \sim x\sin(y)$.

$\propto$ means "proportional to" $f(x,y) \propto x$ in the above example (there is more behaviour not necessarily displayed in a $\propto$ relation).

$\langle(\dots)\rangle$ means the average of the quantity $(\dots)$; see Section 1.2.

$\partial/\partial x$ means the partial derivative (of a function) with respect to x, other independent variables being held constant; see Section 5.1.

$|\dots|$ means "the absolute value of". For complex numbers, it is more usual to say "modulus of".

Physical quantities:

Constant	Symbol	Magnitude	Unit
Planck's constant/2π	$\hbar$	1.05×10^{-34}	J s
Charge on electron	e	1.6×10^{-19}	C
Mass of electron	m_e	9.11×10^{-31}	kg
Mass of proton	m_p	1.67×10^{-27}	kg
Speed of light	c	3.00×10^8	m s^{-1}
Bohr radius	$a_B = 4\pi\epsilon_0\hbar^2/(m_e e^2)$	53.0×10^{-12}	m
Permittivity free space	ϵ_0	8.85×10^{-12}	F m^{-1}

1

Preliminaries — some underlying quantum ideas and mathematical tools

1.1 Moving from classical to quantum

Wavefunctions, probability, uncertainty, wave–particle duality, measurement

Quantum mechanics describes phenomena from the subatomic to the macroscopic, where it reduces to Newtonian mechanics. However, quantum mechanics is constructed on the basis of mathematical and physical ideas different to those of Newton. We shall gradually introduce the ideas of quantum mechanics, largely by example and calculation and, in Chapter 4 of this primer, reconcile them with each other and with the mathematical techniques thus far employed. Initially, we deal with uncertainty and its dynamical consequences, and introduce the idea that a quantum mechanical system can be described in its entirety by a wavefunction. We shall also re-familiarise ourselves with the necessary mathematical tools. Our treatment starts in Chapter 2 with the Schrödinger equation and with illustrative calculations of the properties of simple potentials. In Chapter 3, we deal with more advanced potentials and penetration of quantum particles into classically forbidden regions. Later we introduce the momentum operator, free particle states, expectation values and dynamics. We remain within the Schrödinger "wave mechanics" approach of differential equations and wavefunctions, rather than adopting operators and abstract spaces.

Quantum mechanics and probability in 1-D

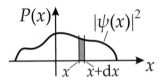

Figure 1.1: A quantum probability density $P(x)$.

A quantum mechanical system, for instance a single particle such as an electron, can be completely described by a *wavefunction*. We call this function $\psi(x)$, which is a function of position x along one dimension. Later we treat higher dimensions and time. It is denoted by the Greek letter "psi", which is pronounced as in the word "psychology". ψ has the interpretation of, when squared, giving the probability density $P(x)$ of finding the particle at the position x; see Fig. 1.1. Density in this case means "the probability per unit length", that is, we multiply by a short length dx to get the probability $P(x)dx$ that the particle is in the interval x to $x + dx$. As always the total probability, here $\int P(x)dx$, must be 1. Most of this book is concerned with real wavefunctions and we have in effect $P(x) = \psi^2(x)$. However quantum mechanics is an intrinsically *complex* subject, that is, its quantities in general involve both the usual real numbers and imaginary numbers. Chapters 4 and 5 address quantum mechanical phenomena that need $i = \sqrt{-1}$, whereupon the probability becomes $P(x) = |\psi(x)|^2$, where $|\ldots|$ means "the absolute value of". For complex numbers, it is more usual to say "modulus of". To be unambiguous we shall write $|\psi(x)|^2$, though the simple square is mostly all we mean.

Uncertainty in quantum mechanics

Knowing the wavefunction (the aim of much of this book) evidently only tells us the probability of finding the particle at a position x. To this extent quantum mechanics is not certain — we can only say that the outcome of many measurements of position would be distributed as $P(x)$ as in, for example, Fig. 1.1. We shall see however at the end that $\psi(x)$ evolves deterministically in time. We shall also encounter the celebrated Heisenberg uncertainty principle:

$$\Delta x . \Delta p \geq \tfrac{1}{2}\hbar, \tag{1.1}$$

where Δx denotes the standard deviation (uncertainty) of x, and equivalently Δp for the momentum p in the x-direction. The quantity $\hbar$ is Planck's constant divided by 2π and is one of the fundamental constants of nature: $\hbar = 1.05 \times 10^{-34}$ J s. Rearranging gives us $\Delta p \geq \tfrac{1}{2}\hbar/\Delta x$, an inverse relation which says that as the uncertainty in position becomes small ($\Delta x \to 0$), then the uncertainty in momentum, Δp, gets very large. Speaking loosely, if we confine a quantum particle in space it moves violently about. We cannot know both spatial and motional information at the same time beyond a certain limit.

There is another important consequence of uncertainty. For wavefunctions with small average momentum $\langle p \rangle$, Δp is a rough measure of the magnitude of the momentum p of the particle[1]. Given that $p = mv$, with m the mass and v the speed, and that the kinetic energy is $T = \frac{1}{2}mv^2 = p^2/2m$, then

$$T \geq \frac{\hbar^2}{2m}\frac{1}{(\Delta x)^2}. \tag{1.2}$$

As we confine a particle, its energy rises. This "kinetic energy of confinement", as it is known, gives rise, for instance, to atomic structure when the confining agent is electromagnetic attraction and to relativistic particle/anti-particle pair production when the energy scale of T is $\geq 2mc^2$, that is more than twice the Einsteinian rest mass energy equivalent.

Measurement and wave–particle duality in Quantum Mechanics

Quantum mechanical particles having a probability $P(x)$ of being found at x, means that the outcomes of many measurements are distributed in this way. Any given measurement has a definite result that localises the particle to the particular position in question. We say that the wavefunction collapses on measurement. Knowing the position exactly removes any knowledge we might have had about the momentum, as we have seen above. In quantum mechanics physical variables appear in *conjugate pairs*, in fact the combinations that appear together in the uncertainty principle. Position and momentum are a basic pair, of which we cannot be simultaneously certain. Another pair we meet is time[2] and energy. Measurement of one gives a definite result and renders the other uncertain. Notice that momentum is the fundamental quantity, not velocity.

It will turn out that the wavefunction ψ will indeed describe waves, and thus also the fundamentally wave-like phenomena such as diffraction and interference that quantum mechanical particles exhibit. For electrons

---

[1] Consider for instance a particle where the momentum takes the values $+p$ or $-p$. So $\langle p \rangle = 0$. The mean square of the momentum is clearly p^2, and the root mean square, that is, the standard deviation, $\Delta p = p$ simply. If p takes a spread of values, then Δp is not so precisely related to any of the individual p values, but it still gives an idea of the typical size of the momentum.

[2] Time is special as it is not a true dynamical variable.

the appropriate "slits" leading to diffraction and then interference are actually the atoms or molecules in a crystal. They have a characteristic spacing matched to the wavelength of electrons of modest energy. A probability $P(x)$ of finding diffracted particles, for instance, on a plane behind a crystal is reminiscent of the interference patterns developed by light behind a screen with slits. However the detection of a particle falling on this plane will localise it to the specific point of detection — particles are not individually smeared out once measured. Thus a wave-like aspect is required to get a $P(x)$ characteristic of interference, and a particle-like result is observed in individual measurements; this is the celebrated wave–particle duality. In Chapter 4 we show pictures of particles landing on a screen, but distributed as if they were waves!

Figure 1.2: G.P. Thomson — Nobel Prize (1937; with Davisson) for diffraction of electrons as quantum mechanical waves, and J.J. Thomson — Nobel Prize (1906) for work "on conduction of electricity by gases", middle row, 2nd and 4th from left respectively. In this class photo of Cavendish Laboratory research students in 1920 there are four other Nobel prize winners to be identified — see this book's web site for answers.

The electron was discovered as a fundamental particle by J.J. Thomson using apparatus reminiscent of the cathode ray tube as in an old fashioned

TV. His son, G.P. Thomson, a generation later discovered electron as a wave using diffraction (through celluloid); see Fig. 1.2. Both father and son separately received Nobel Prizes in physics for discovering the opposite of each other! J.J. was Cavendish Professor in Cambridge (the supervisor and predecessor of Rutherford), and was Master of Trinity College, Cambridge. G.P. made his Nobel discovery in Aberdeen, did further fundamental work at Imperial College, and was Master of Corpus Christi College in Cambridge.

Potentials and forces

Unlike the standard treatments of classical mechanics in terms of forces, quantum mechanics deals more naturally in terms of energies. In particular, the role of a force is replaced by its potential energy. Forces between particles, or for instance those exerted by a spring, do work when the particles move or a spring changes length. The energy stored in the field or spring is potential energy $V(x)$, a function of separation, extension, etc. x. Movement of the point of application of the force, f, *against* its direction by $-dx$ gives an *increase* in the stored energy $dV = -fdx$ ("force times distance"), that is, force is given by $f = -dV/dx$. Note the $-$ sign. One speaks simply of a potential $V(x)$ which, if it changes with position, gives rise to forces.

Famous examples of potentials include

$$V(x) = +\frac{Q_1 Q_2}{4\pi\epsilon_0 x} \qquad \text{(Coulomb/electric)}$$

$$= -\frac{Gm_1 m_2}{x} \qquad \text{(gravitation)}$$

$$= +\tfrac{1}{2}qx^2, \qquad \text{(harmonic)}$$

where the first gives the Coulomb repulsive/attractive force between two charges Q_1 and Q_2 depending on their relative signs, and the second gives the gravitational attractive force between two masses m_1 and m_2, the charges and masses being a distance x apart. The third potential gives the retractive force $-qx$ when a spring is stretched by x away from its natural length. The constants that determine the scale of the potential, ϵ_0, G and q are the permittivity of free space, the gravitational constant and the spring constant, respectively. We shall explore quantum motion and energies in potentials of various shapes.

It is important to think about and solve the problems posed in the text. Mostly they will have at least some hint to their solution. The problems

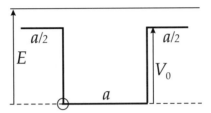

Figure 1.3: A finite square well of depth V_0.

in part illustrate the principles under discussion. But physics and maths are subjects only really understood when one can "do". Problems are the only route to this understanding, and also give fluency in the core (mathematical) skills of physics. So repeat for yourself even the problems where complete or partial solutions have been given.

Exercise 1.1: Derive from the electric, gravitational and harmonic potentials their force laws. Explain the sign of the forces — is it what you expect? Take care over the definition of the zero of potential. Does the position where the potential is zero matter?

Subsequent problems explore the shift from using forces to potentials in analysing a problem. For instance, to calculate the change in speed of a particle, you might have considered a force-displacement curve. This is a diagram which tells you what forces are acting as a function of the position of the particle. In fact, one would need to know the area under the curve, which amounts to the change of energy of the particle (from potential energy to kinetic energy or vice versa). We can avoid having to know such detail by simply using the potential energy graph. These ideas are best illustrated by the following examples.

Exercise 1.2: Consider a particle of mass m passing a potential well of width a, as shown in Fig. 1.3. The particle has total energy $E > V_0$, the depth of the well. Calculate the time taken by the particle to traverse the figure.

Solution: First, we note that the well is a schematic of the energies and we are asked to use energies directly rather than forces. Secondly, the nature of the forces is irrelevant — this is the advantage of an energy approach. The diagram is not describing a dip in a physical landscape.

In the regions outside the well, the kinetic energy is the difference between the total energy E and the potential energy V_0

$$\frac{1}{2}mv^2 = E - V_0. \tag{1.3}$$

So the speed is given by $v = \sqrt{\frac{2(E-V_0)}{m}}$. Inside the well, all the energy is entirely kinetic and so the speed is $v' = \sqrt{\frac{2E}{m}}$. Making use of the definition of speed, we find the total time

$$t = \sqrt{\frac{ma^2}{2}} \left(\frac{1}{\sqrt{E}} + \frac{1}{\sqrt{E - V_0}} \right). \tag{1.4}$$

Exercise 1.3: A particle of mass m slides down, under gravity, a smooth ramp which is inclined at angle θ to the horizontal. At the bottom, it is joined smoothly to a similar ramp rising at the same angle θ to the horizontal to form a V-shaped surface. If the particle slides smoothly around the join, determine the period of oscillation, T, in terms of the initial horizontal displacement x_0 from the centre join. Note the shape of the potential well.

Hint: We see that the potential well appears as a sloping line similar to the one along which the particle is constrained to move. It is only this linear slope at angle θ to the horizontal, that happens to resemble the potential energy graph of the same shape, which misleads us into thinking that we can see the potential energy. The potential energy is a concept, represented pictorially by a graph and the shape of the graph happens, in some cases, to resemble the mechanical system.

The distinction between the actual landscape (flat) and the potential is clear in the case of a quadratic potential. See Fig. 3.4 on page 55.

Exercise 1.4: A particle moves in a potential $V(x) = \frac{1}{2}qx^2$. If it has total energy $E = E_0$ give an expression for its velocity as a function of position $v(x)$. What is the amplitude of its motion?

Exercise 1.5: The potential energy of a particle of mass m as a function of its position along the x axis is as shown in Figure 1.4.
(a) Sketch a graph of the force versus position in the x direction which acts

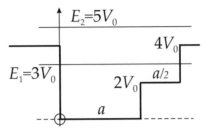

Figure 1.4: A stepped rectangular potential well

on a particle moving in this potential well with its vertical steps. Why is this potential unphysical?

(b) Sketch a more realistic force versus position curve for a particle in this potential well. For a particle moving from $x = 0$ to $x = \frac{3a}{2}$, which way does the force act on the particle? If the particle was moving in the opposite direction, which way would the force be acting on the particle?

Hint: Take care over the physical meaning of the potential energy. It can look misleadingly like the physical picture of a particle sliding off a high shelf, down a very steep slope and then sliding along the floor, reflecting off the left hand wall and then back up the slope. This is too literal an interpretation since, for example, the potential change might be due to an electrostatic effect rather than a gravitational one, and the time spent moving up or down the slope is due to artificially putting in an extra vertical dimension in a problem which is about motion in only one dimension. An example of where there is literally motion vertically as well as horizontally, is that of a frictionless bead threaded on a parabolic wire. The motion is not the same as in the one-dimensional simple harmonic motion of Ex. 1.4. Although the potential energy is expressible in the form $\frac{1}{2}qx^2$ due to the constraint of the wire, the kinetic energy involves both the x and y variables.

Exercise 1.6: Consider again the particle in Ex. 1.5. If it has a total mechanical energy E equal to $3V_0$, calculate the period for a complete oscillation.

Quantum mechanics in the world around us

Quantum effects are mostly manifested on a length scale much smaller than we can observe with light and hence are not directly part of our everyday world. Indeed we shall see that quantum mechanics takes us far from our common experience. A particle can be in two places at the same time — it must pass through at least two slits for interference to occur — and we shall see the need to think of them as having a wave–particle duality of character. But our world is dominated by the macroscopic effects of quanta. The conductivity of metals and semiconductors is entirely dominated by quantum effects and without them there would be no semiconductor age with computers, consumer electronics, digital cameras, telecommunications, modern medical equipment, or lasers with which to read digital discs. Atomic and molecular physics, chemistry, superconductivity and superfluidity, electron transfer in biology are all dominated by quantum mechanics. It is with quantum mechanical waves, in an electron microscope, that we first saw the atomic world. The ability of quantum particles to tunnel through classically forbidden regions is exploited in the scanning tunnelling microscope to see individual atoms.

We shall explore such fundamental effects. For instance, we shall see how quantum particles explore classically forbidden regions where they have negative kinetic energy and should really not venture. We shall even at the end quantise a model of electromagnetic standing waves and see how photons and phonons arise. However fundamental the phenomena we examine, and those that more advanced courses deal with, these effects have all had a revolutionary influence in the last century through their applications to technology, and have fashioned the world in which we live.

1.2 Mathematical preliminaries for quantum mechanics

Probability, trigonometric and exponential functions, calculus, differential equations, plotting functions and qualitative solutions to transcendental equations

Mathematics suffuses all of physics. Indeed some of the most important mathematics was developed to describe physical problems: for example Newton's description of gravitational attraction and motion required his invention of calculus. If you are good at maths, and especially if you enjoy using it (for instance in mechanics), then higher physics is probably for you even if this is not yet clear to you from school physics. This book depends on maths largely established by the end of the penultimate year at school. We simply sketch what you have learned more thoroughly already, but might not yet have practised much or used in real problems. So we assume exposure to trigonometric and exponential functions, and to differentiation and integration in calculus. We later introduce some more elaborate forms of what you know already — for instance the extension of algebra to the imaginary number i and its use in the exponential function, and differentiation with respect to one variable while keeping another independent variables constant (partial differentiation).

Practice is the only path to becoming good at maths and to eventually finding its execution and applications simple. The examples given throughout these notes are designed to illustrate the physics, but more importantly they will give you fluency and confidence in maths so that it is never an issue in your understanding the physics.

Probability

Wavefunctions generate probabilities, for instance that of finding a particle in a particular position. We shall use probabilities throughout these notes, taking averages, variances etc. Familiar averages over a discrete set of outcomes i are written, for instance:

$$\langle x \rangle = \sum_i x_i p_i \quad \text{and} \quad \langle f(x) \rangle = \sum_i f(x_i) p_i \,. \tag{1.5}$$

Here $\langle\ \rangle$ around a quantity means its average over the probabilities p_i. This is called the *expectation value* of the quantity. When outcomes are continuously distributed, we replace the p_i by a probability density (probability per unit length) $P(x)$ which gives a probability $P(x)dx$ that an outcome falls in the interval x to $x + dx$. Just as the discrete probabilities must add up to 1, so do the continuous probabilities:

$$\sum_i p_i = 1 \rightarrow \int P(x)dx = 1 \,. \tag{1.6}$$

Such probabilities are said to be normalised. If the probability is not yet normalised, we can still use it but we must divide our averages by $\int P(x)dx$, which is in effect just performing the normalisation. You will see that in some problems it pays to delay this normalisation process in the hope that it eventually cancels between numerator and denominator. Thus averages (1.5) become

$$\langle x \rangle = \int x P(x)dx \quad \text{and} \quad \langle f(x) \rangle = \int f(x)P(x)dx \,. \tag{1.7}$$

Exercise 1.7: The variance σ^2 in the values of x is the average of the square of the deviations of x from its mean, that is,

$$\sigma^2 = \langle (x - \langle x \rangle)^2 \rangle .$$

Prove the above agrees with the standard result $\sigma^2 = \langle x^2 \rangle - \langle x \rangle^2$ for both discrete and continuous x.

Essential functions for quantum mechanics

We shall see that a particle in a constant potential $V(x) = V_0$, say, is represented by a wavefunction $\psi \propto \sin(kx)$, where $\propto$ means "proportional to" (that is, we have left off the constant of proportionality between ψ and $\sin(kx)$). The argument of the sine function, the combination kx, can be thought of as an angle, say $\theta = kx$. It must be dimensionless, as the argument for all functions must be — this is a good physics check of algebra! Hence k must have the dimensions of $1/\text{length}$ and we shall return to its meaning in Chapter 2.3. ψ could equally be represented by $\cos(kx)$ with a change of phase. We shall constantly use properties of trigonometric functions, among the simplest being:

$$\sin^2 \theta = 1 - \cos^2 \theta \tag{1.8}$$

$$\cos(2\theta) = 2\cos^2 \theta - 1 = 1 - 2\sin^2 \theta \tag{1.9}$$

$$\sin(2\theta) = 2 \sin \theta \cos \theta \tag{1.10}$$

$$\tan \theta = \sin \theta / \cos \theta \tag{1.11}$$

$$\sin \theta + \sin \phi = 2 \sin \left(\frac{\theta + \phi}{2} \right) \cos \left(\frac{\theta - \phi}{2} \right) \tag{1.12}$$

The double angle relations (1.9) and (1.10) are sometimes used in integrals in rearranged form, e.g. $\sin^2 \theta = \frac{1}{2}(1 - \cos(2\theta))$. The addition formula (1.12) is used when adding waves together.

In quantum mechanics it is possible to have negative kinetic energy, something that is classically forbidden since clearly our familiar form is $T = p^2/2m \geq 0$. If while $T < 0$ the potential is also constant, $V(x) = V_0$, then the wavefunction will have the form $\psi \propto e^{-kx}$ or $\propto e^{kx}$, depending on whether x is increasing or decreasing respectively. The function e^x is the exponential. We shall find sin, cos and exp as functions whose oscillations in wells, and decay away from wells, describe localised quantum mechanical particles.

The *Gaussian* function $e^{-x^2/2\sigma^2}$ has a very special place in the whole of physics. The form given is the standard form complete with the factor of 2 and its characteristic width σ for reasons made clear in Ex. 1.14. It is the wavefunction for the quantum simple harmonic oscillator in its ground state and is also the wavefunction with the minimal uncertainty. We return to it at the end of Chapter 3.

Exercise 1.8: Plot $e^{-x^2/2\sigma^2}$ for a range of positive and negative x. Label important points on the x axis (including where the function is $1/e$) and the y axis. Pay special attention to $x = 0$, including slope and curvature there. What is the effect on the graph of varying σ?

A little calculus — differentiation

The first derivative of the function $f(x)$, denoted by $\mathrm{d}f/\mathrm{d}x$, is the slope of f. Figure 1.5 shows the tangent to the curve $f(x)$ and, in a triangle, how the limit as $\delta x \to 0$ of the ratio of the infinitesimal rise δf to the increment δx along the x axis gives $\tan\theta$ and hence the slope of $f(x)$ at a point. Vitally important is the second derivative $\mathrm{d}^2 f/\mathrm{d}x^2$ since this leads to the quantum mechanical kinetic energy, T. It is the rate of change of the slope. Figure 1.5 shows regions of increasing/decreasing slopes and hence positive/negative second derivatives. The second derivative is in effect the rate

Figure 1.5: The gradient $\mathrm{d}f/\mathrm{d}x = \tan\theta$ of the function $f(x)$. The second derivative $\mathrm{d}^2 f/\mathrm{d}x^2$ is positive at the minimum where the slope is increasing with x. The curvature, $1/R$, derives from the circular arc, of radius R, fitted to $f(x)$ at x.

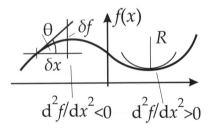

at which the curve deviates from its local tangent. We shall also loosely refer to it as the "curvature". Figure 1.5 shows an arc of a circle of radius R fitted to a minimal point, a point of zero slope where the second derivative is exactly $\mathrm{d}^2 f/\mathrm{d}x^2 = 1/R$. Away from minima or maxima, but for not too great a slope, the curvature is approximately the second derivative [3].

---

[3] A precise definition for the curvature is $1/R = \mathrm{d}^2 f/\mathrm{d}x^2/(1 + (\mathrm{d}f/\mathrm{d}x)^2)^{3/2}$ which takes account of an increment δx not being the same as an increment of length along the curve.

We require derivatives of the most common functions encountered in quantum mechanics:

$$\frac{d}{dx}\sin(kx) = k\cos(kx) \tag{1.13}$$

$$\frac{d}{dx}\cos(kx) = -k\sin(kx) \tag{1.14}$$

$$\frac{d}{dx}e^{kx} = ke^{kx}. \tag{1.15}$$

The latter is a definition of the exponential function — the function that is its own derivative. To see this relation, we make the substitution $u = kx$ into Eq. (1.15). The derivatives become $\frac{d}{dx} = \frac{du}{dx}\frac{d}{du} = k\frac{d}{du}$ and so we find that $\frac{d}{du}e^u = e^u$. Another common function in physics is the inverse function to the exponential — the natural logarithm. Consider the curve $y = e^x$. The inverse function is

$$x = e^y. \tag{1.16}$$

To see this we sketch both functions on the same axes, Fig. 1.6. We write the

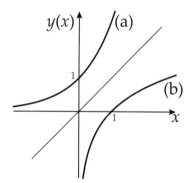

Figure 1.6: Plots of (a) $y(x) = e^x$ and (b) $y(x) = \ln(x)$. They are reflections of each other in the line $y = x$ and thus one can think of (b) as $x = e^y$.

solution to Eq. (1.16) as $y = \ln x$. The derivative may be found by making use of the result for derivatives of inverse functions, viz. $\frac{dy}{dx} = 1/(\frac{dx}{dy})$. Since $\frac{dx}{dy} = e^y = x$ we have

$$\frac{d}{dx}\ln x = \frac{1}{x}. \tag{1.17}$$

Exercise 1.9: Plot $\sin(kx)$, $\cos(kx)$, $e^{\pm kx}$ and $\ln(kx)$ for a range of positive and negative x. Label important points (e.g. intersections with axes, maxima and minima) on the x and y axes. What happens to these points and the graph if you change k? Revise elementary properties of the exponential and logarithmic functions. What are $(e^x)^2$, e^x/e^y, $a\ln x$ and $\ln x + \ln y$?

At http://www.periphyseos.org is a dynamic applet which shows the effect of changing k.

We often need to differentiate the product of two functions:

$$\frac{d}{dx}\left(g(x).h(x)\right) = \frac{dg(x)}{dx}.h(x) + g(x).\frac{dh(x)}{dx}, \qquad (1.18)$$

which is the *product rule*.

Sometimes we shall differentiate a function of a function for which one requires the *chain rule*.

Exercise 1.10: Use the chain rule to show that $\frac{d}{dx}e^{-x^2/2\sigma^2} = -\frac{x}{\sigma^2}e^{-x^2/2\sigma^2}$. Plot the derivative of the Gaussian on the same graph as the Gaussian you plotted in Ex. 1.8. This result helps in the integration by parts in Ex. 1.14.

Solution: The chain rule allows us to differentiate a function of a function, that is $\frac{d}{dx}f(g(x))$. Differentiate the function $f(g)$ with respect to its argument g, and then differentiate g with respect to its argument x, thus getting $\frac{d}{dx}f(g(x)) = \frac{df}{dg} \cdot \frac{dg}{dx}$, both parts of the right hand side being functions ultimately of x. Here f is the exponential function e^g, and $g(x) = -x^2/2\sigma^2$, whence $df/dg = f$ and $dg/dx = -x/\sigma^2$ and we obtain the desired result. Plot the graph.

A little calculus — integration

Integration is the reverse operation to differentiation. Geometrically, it gives the area, A, under a curve between the points $x = a$ and b in Fig. 1.7. We write the integral as $A(a,b) = \int_a^b f(x)dx$ and can think of it as the limit of the sum (Σ) of infinitesimal component areas. $A(a,b)$ can be divided into a very large number of very thin rectangular slices of width dx and height $f(x)$. Each element in the sum $A = \sum_a^b f(x)dx$ is one of the infinitesimal areas shown in Fig. 1.7. It is clear that since areas add, then $\int_a^b f(x)dx + \int_b^c f(x)dx = \int_a^c f(x)dx$. These are examples of *definite* integrals, that is with definite limits specified. Where the limits are not

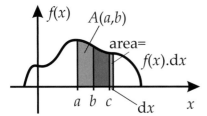

Figure 1.7: Integration gives the area under a curve of the function. Integrals can be added, thus $A(a,b) + A(b,c) = A(a,c)$.

given these integrals are termed indefinite. Commonly, there is no distinction made between independent and dummy variables. For example, $\int e^x dx = e^x$ has x as the same variable for both sides. We shall not abuse this notation. For instance,

$$\int^x \sin(kz)dz = -\frac{1}{k}\cos(kx) + c_1 \tag{1.19}$$

$$\int^x \cos(kz)dz = \frac{1}{k}\sin(kx) + c_2 \tag{1.20}$$

$$\int^x e^{kz}dz = \frac{1}{k}e^{kx} + c_3. \tag{1.21}$$

Note that an arbitrary constant (c_1, c_2, c_3 in the above) then arises in each integration. It can be thought of related to the starting point of the integration which has been left indefinite. To reconcile the absent lower limit to the appearance of an arbitrary constant, consider as an example $\int_a^x e^z dz = e^x - e^a$. If a is an arbitrary constant, then so is the constant e^a. Upon differentiation these constants are removed. The variable of integration, z, is a dummy variable — any symbol can be used. This is identical to the dummy index used in discrete sums. For instance, the sum $\sum_i x_i$ is the same as $\sum_j x_j$. The only difference is that z in the former example is a continuous variable whereas i and j are discrete.

Exercise 1.11: Confirm by differentiation of the right hand sides of Eqs. (1.19–1.21) that, in these cases at least, differentiation is indeed the reverse process from integration; that is, $\frac{d}{dx}\int^x f(z)dz = f(x)$ in the above examples.

The result is generally true; take $I(x + dx) = \int^{x+dx} f(z)dz$ and subtract from it $I(x) = \int^x f(z)dz$. Use the ideas in Fig. 1.7 of adding or subtracting integrals to construct $\frac{dI}{dx} = \lim_{dx \to 0} \frac{I(x+dx)-I(x)}{dx}$. The numerator is clearly $A(x, x + dx)$ which, from the definition of integration, is in this limit

$f(x).dx$. Putting this result in and cancelling the dx factors top and bottom, one obtains $\frac{dI}{dx} = f(x)$.

Integration by parts

Integration by parts is frequently useful in quantum mechanics. It can be thought of as the reverse of differentiation of a product. Integrating Eq. (1.18) gives

$$\int_a^b \frac{d}{dx}[g(x).h(x)]\,dx = \int_a^b \frac{dg(x)}{dx}.h(x)dx + \int_a^b g(x).\frac{dh(x)}{dx}dx. \quad (1.22)$$

Rearranging we find that

$$\int_a^b g(x).\frac{dh(x)}{dx}dx = [g(x).h(x)]_a^b - \int_a^b \frac{dg(x)}{dx}.h(x)dx. \quad (1.23)$$

Notice that h on the right hand side can be regarded as the indefinite integral of the dh/dx factor on the left hand side, that is $h(x) = \int^x \frac{dh}{dz}dz$. For clarity rewriting g as $u(x)$ and dh/dx as $v(x)$, one can rewrite in a form easier to remember and apply:

$$\int_a^b u(x).v(x)dx = \left[u(x).\left(\int^x v(z)dz\right)\right]_a^b - \int_a^b \left(\frac{du}{dx}\right).\left(\int^x v(z)dz\right)dx.$$

$$(1.24)$$

Be fluent with the use of the result. Our experience shows that it is best to remember it for use directly along the lines of

> "to integrate a product (uv), integrate one part (v) and evaluate this integral times the other function between the given limits, that is giving the first term on the right. Take away the integral of [(the integral already done)×(the derivative of the other factor)], giving the second term on the right."

Judiciously choose the easier of u and v to integrate. For instance,

$$\int_0^\infty xe^{-kx}dx = \left[-x\frac{1}{k}e^{-kx}\right]_0^\infty + \int_0^\infty \frac{1}{k}e^{-kx}dx, \quad (1.25)$$

where $u(x) = x$ and $v(x) = e^{-kx}$, with $du/dx = 1$ and $\int^x v(z)dz = -\frac{1}{k}e^{-kx}$. The first term of the right hand side of (1.25) is zero since it vanishes at both limits, and the second term is $1/k^2$ on doing the exponential integral a second time, and this is the answer.

Exercise 1.12: Integrate $\int_0^\infty x^n e^{-x} dx$ once by parts. The result suggests repetition until the final result. What well-known function results?

Exercise 1.13: Integrate $\int_0^{\frac{\pi}{2}} x^2 \sin x \, dx$ and $\int_0^{\frac{\pi}{2}} x^2 \cos x \, dx$.

The split into u and v can require delicacy! For example, the integral $\int_{-\infty}^\infty x^2 e^{-x^2/2\sigma^2} dx$ can be written as $\int u.v dx = \int (-\sigma^2 x). \left(-\frac{x}{\sigma^2} e^{-x^2/2\sigma^2} \right) dx$. Identifying $v(x)$ as the second factor, the integral $\int^x v(z) dz = e^{-x^2/2\sigma^2}$ is easy; see in Ex. 1.10 the differentiation of this answer back to the starting point, and $du/dx = -\sigma^2$ is also easy. The integral has been reduced to another one which does not have a simple answer, but that itself is not necessarily a difficulty — a problem delayed is sometimes a problem solved!

Exercise 1.14: If $P(x) \propto e^{-x^2/2\sigma^2}$, what is the average $\langle x^2 \rangle$?

This Gaussian result is found throughout physics and is worth remembering:

> "From a Gaussian probability written in its standard form $P(x) \propto e^{-x^2/2\sigma^2}$, one reads off the mean square value of x as being σ^2, that is, the number appearing in the denominator of the exponent, taking care to re-arrange slightly if the required factor of two is not directly apparent."

What would be the mean square value of x be if the probability were $P(x) \propto e^{-2x^2/b^2}$? Answer: $\langle x^2 \rangle = b^2/4$.

The reader eager to get on to quantum mechanics could skip the next problems, quickly revise differential equations, and jump to Chapter 2. It will be obvious to you when it is to your advantage to return to this exercise.

Exercise 1.15: Evaluate $N = \int_0^L \sin^2(\frac{\pi x}{L}) dx$ and $\frac{1}{N} \int_0^L x^2 \sin^2(\frac{\pi x}{L}) dx$.
Hint: Use a double angle result and integration by parts. $N = L/2$, a result that is rather general for the integration of squares of sine and cosine through intervals that defined as being between various of their nodes. After studying quantum wells you might like to return to the choice π/L for the coefficient of x in the argument of sine. The second result is

$L^2 \left(\frac{1}{3} - \frac{1}{2\pi^2} \right)$. Given your result for N, then $\frac{1}{N} \sin^2(\pi x/L)$ would be an acceptable probability $P(x)$. What is $\langle x \rangle$? What is the variance of x?

Exercise 1.16: Integrate the functions $\ln x$, $\frac{\ln x}{x^2}$ and $\frac{\ln(\sin x)}{\cos^2 x}$.

Differential equations

Most of physics involves differential equations and they certainly underpin quantum mechanics. Such equations involve the derivatives of functions as well or instead of the usual familiar algebraic operators in simple equations such as powers. The first differential equations we meet are those of free motion, or motion with constant acceleration, such as free fall with g. Thus force = mass times acceleration is the differential equation $m\,dv/dt = mg$. It is easily integrated once with respect to time t: the right hand side is constant in time and gives mgt. The left hand side has the derivative nullified by integration to give mv + constant. Cancelling the masses, gives $v = v_0 + gt$. We have taken the initial speed (at $t = 0$) as v_0, that is, we have fixed the constant of integration by using an initial condition. More generally, these are termed *boundary conditions*. Rewriting the answer as $dz/dt = v_0 + gt$, where z is the distance fallen down, we can integrate both sides again to yield $z = v_0 t + \frac{1}{2} g t^2$, where we have taken the next constant of integration, the position z_0 at $t = 0$, to be zero. This familiar result of kinematics is actually the result of solving a differential equation with a second order derivative since we could have written our starting equation as $d^2 z/dt^2 = g$.

Exercise 1.17: For the mass under free fall described above, sketch on the same axes the acceleration $\frac{dv}{dt}$, velocity v and displacement z as a function of time.

Simple harmonic motion

Ubiquitous throughout physics is simple harmonic motion (SHM) or the simple harmonic oscillator (SHO) which for instance in dynamics results when a particle of mass m is acted on by a spring exerting a force $-qz$ where now z denotes the particle's displacement from the origin. The corresponding potential giving rise to the force is harmonic — see the discussion of potentials on page 5. The $-$ sign indicates that the force is restoring, that is, opposite in direction to the displacement, and q is Hooke's constant. Newton's second law is $f = ma$ with the acceleration $a = \frac{dv}{dt}$ being the time derivative of the velocity, that is, of $v = \frac{dz}{dt}$. Using the Hookean force, one obtains the equation of motion

$$m\frac{d^2z}{dt^2} = -qz \quad \text{or} \quad \frac{d^2z}{dt^2} = -\omega^2 z, \tag{1.26}$$

where the angular frequency, ω, will be discussed below and is clearly $\omega = \sqrt{q/m}$. This equation describes oscillations of the particle here, but in a general form also those of an electric field in electromagnetic radiation, or the quantum fields in quantum electrodynamics. Thus differential equations differ from the usual kinds of algebraic equations since they involve derivatives of the function. The highest derivative in (1.26) is a second derivative and so (1.26) is called a second order (ordinary) differential equation. The "ordinary" means there is only one independent variable, t here. We shall later meet cases of more than one independent variable which give rise to "partial" differential equations.

An honourable and perfectly legitimate method of solving differential equations is to guess a solution and try it out. Guesses can often be very well informed and hence this is not entirely magic!

Exercise 1.18: Inspect Eqs. (1.13–1.15) and differentiate each side again. Confirm that for $f = \sin(kx)$ and $\cos(kx)$, and separately for $f = e^{\pm kx}$, one has respectively the similar results:

$$\frac{d^2f}{dx^2} = -k^2 f \quad \text{and} \quad \frac{d^2f}{dx^2} = k^2 f. \tag{1.27}$$

In a mysterious way e^{kx} is like $\sin(kx)$ or $\cos(kx)$, but with k^2 replaced by $-k^2$. This turns out to be true, but there is the little matter of a squared number becoming negative! ($5^2 = 25$ and $(-5)^2 = 25$ too; how would one get a result of -25?) We treat imaginary and complex numbers in Chapter 4.1 which could also be read now if desired.

Considering time t rather than x as the independent variable, one can confirm that two solutions for SHM (Eq. (1.26)) are

$$z(t) = z_s \sin(\omega t), \quad z(t) = z_c \cos(\omega t). \tag{1.28}$$

Since sine and cosine repeat when $\omega t = 2\pi$, that is, after a period $t = T = 2\pi/\omega$, then rearrangement shows that $\omega = 2\pi/T \equiv 2\pi\nu$ — the angular frequency where $\nu = 1/T$ is the usual frequency. The amplitudes z_s and z_c of oscillation are arbitrary and indeed the general solution would be $z(t) = z_s \sin(\omega t) + z_c \cos(\omega t)$, which is an arbitrary combination of the oscillatory components differing in phase by $\pi/2$ or 90 degrees.

We have seen in the second order differential equation (1.26), a constant is introduced every time we integrate. Two integrations and thus two constants are required to get a general solution. How do we fix these constants? "Boundary conditions", in this case two, and in general as many as the order of the equation, are required to fully solve differential equations. Here for instance, at $t = 0$ we have $z(t = 0) = 0$ and $dz/dt = v_0$ (the particle is initially at the origin with velocity v_0). The first condition demands that $z_c = 0$ (recall what $\sin(0)$ and $\cos(0)$ are). The second condition gives

$$v_0 = \left.\frac{dz}{dt}\right|_{t=0} = \omega z_s \cos(\omega t)|_{t=0} = \omega z_s ,$$

that is $z_s = v_0/\omega$. See also the simple example above of integrating the differential equation of free fall. Note that the period ($T = 2\pi/\omega$) is independent of the amplitude: only the ratio between the inertia factor (the mass) and the elasticity factor (the spring constant) matters. This is generally not true. See Ex. 1.3 where the period increases with amplitude and Ex. 1.33 for more exotic behaviour. Consult Sect. 3.2 for further discussion of classical SHM.

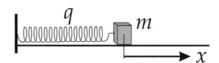

Figure 1.8: A mass on a light spring.

Exercise 1.19: A mass m, attached to a light spring of constant q, slides on a horizontal surface of negligible friction, as shown in Figure 1.8. The mass is displaced through a distance x_0 from the equilibrium position and released. Write down Newton's 2nd law as applied to the displaced mass.

A clock is started at some later time and the dependence of the displacement on time is given by $x(t) = x_0 \sin(\omega t + \phi)$. Act on the time dependent displacement $x(t)$ with the operator $\frac{d^2}{dt^2}$. You will see that the same function is obtained up to a multiplicative constant. Obtain the constant and relate it to the result of Newton's 2nd Law.

Sketch a graph of the system's potential energy versus displacement.

Exponentially decaying motion

If friction dominates, that is, if there is no or insufficient restoring force, we have instead exponential instead of sinusoidal motion.

Exercise 1.20: A block sliding on a surface suffers a retarding force proportional to its velocity, $f = -\mu v$, where μ is a constant. Show that $dv/dt = -(\mu/m)v$ and solve the equation subject to $v(t = 0) = v_0$. What is the displacement as a function of time? Sketch the block's displacement, velocity and acceleration as a function of time on the same axes.

Solution: Applying Newton II gives $m\frac{dv}{dt} = -\mu v$. This is a first order separable differential equation. The solution can be found by either comparison with radioactive decay or by separating variables. Performing the latter yields $\frac{dv}{v} = -\frac{\mu}{m}dt$. Integrating and inserting the boundary condition gives

$$\int_{v_0}^{v} \frac{dv}{v} = -\frac{\mu}{m} \int_0^t dt \tag{1.29}$$

$$\ln\left(\frac{v}{v_0}\right) = -\frac{\mu}{m}t \tag{1.30}$$

$$v = v_0 e^{-\frac{\mu}{m}t}. \tag{1.31}$$

Note that there is only one boundary condition since it is a first order differential equation. Check that this is indeed a solution to the differential equation (and the initial condition) by direct substitution. A further integration produces the displacement $\frac{mv_0}{\mu}\left(1 - e^{-\frac{\mu}{m}t}\right)$ at time t.

Exercise 1.21: A model for a parachutist's downward speed $v(t)$ at time t in free fall after jumping out is given by

$$m\frac{dv}{dt} = mg - kv. \tag{1.32}$$

Explain the physical origin of each of the terms. Solve the differential equation (1.32) given his initial speed is zero when he jumps out. What is his terminal velocity?

We return to very general and important aspects of differential equations in Sect. 2.3 on Sturm–Liouville theory.

Interference of waves

We have seen that the general solution to the SHM equation (1.26) is $z(t) = z_s \sin(\omega t) + z_c \cos(\omega t)$. That is, any sum or linear combination of $z(t) = \sin(\omega t)$ and $z(t) = \cos(\omega t)$ is also a solution. This is a general property of linear differential equations. Linear means that there are no powers in the derivatives or the function z. The differential equation governing waves is also linear in the same way. And thus waves can add or superpose to give other composite waves that are also solutions of the same equation.

When we superpose two waves, in some places the disturbances add, in other places they subtract, depending on the relative phase of the two quantities being added. The phase might depend on position such as in the two slit experiment. Here we have two separated but identical sources of waves which travel to an observation screen. At a general point on the screen the distances travelled by the two sets of waves will be different. Let us take two extremal examples. First, if the path difference between waves from the double slits to a given observation point is exactly a wavelength, the waves add in phase and give a maximum of intensity (known as constructive interference). Conversely, if the path difference is a half wavelength, one has destructive interference and thus a node, a position of zero intensity, on the observation screen. This process of wave interference occurs for any waves travelling in any direction through the same region of space. See the 2-slit experiment of Fig. 4.3 on page 70. Another example is standing waves which are produced by the interference of two identical counterpropagating waves:

Exercise 1.22: Show that the waves $\sin(kx + \phi/2)$ and $\sin(kx - \phi/2)$, differing in phase by ϕ, add to give a resultant wave $2\sin(kx)\cos(\phi)$. Consider the cases of being in phase ($\phi = 0$) and in anti-phase ($\phi = \pi$) when these two waves interfere.

Waves on a stretched string

Consider a string under tension T and of mass per unit length μ. It is anchored at $x = 0$ and $x = a$; see Fig. 1.9. For small sideways displacements $\psi(x)$ at the position x the length changes little and the tension remains T. One can show that the envelope $\psi(x)$ of standing or stationary waves obeys

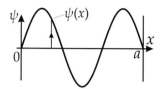

Figure 1.9: A snapshot of standing waves on a stretched string at a particular time. For snapshots of the string at other times, see Fig. 5.6. The transverse displacement is $\psi(x)$.

the equation

$$\frac{d^2\psi}{dx^2} = -\frac{\mu}{T}\omega^2\psi. \tag{1.33}$$

See Sect. 5.3 for a derivation of the full motion, of which this is one limit. For standing sound waves in a tube, $\psi(x)$ would be the pressure that varies with position x along the tube. The wave speed is $c = \sqrt{T/\mu}$ and $\omega = 2\pi\nu$ connects the angular and conventional frequencies, ω and ν. Thus in the above equation

$$\frac{\omega}{c} = \frac{2\pi\nu}{c} = \frac{2\pi}{\lambda} = k, \tag{1.34}$$

where these rearrangements employ $\nu\lambda = c$ with λ the wavelength. The final definition $k = 2\pi/\lambda$ introduces the wavevector that is so ubiquitous in quantum mechanics and optics. Thus the standing wave equation becomes

$$\frac{d^2\psi}{dx^2} = -k^2\psi, \tag{1.35}$$

which is the form of Eq. (1.27). Its solutions are $\sin(kx)$ and $\cos(kx)$. Figure 1.9 shows that since $\psi(0) = 0$ we have to discard the $\cos(kx)$ solutions, since they are non-zero at $x = 0$, in favour of $\sin(kx)$ solutions that naturally vanish at $x = 0$. Equally in Fig. 1.9, to ensure $\psi(x = a) = 0$, it is necessary for an integer number of half wavelengths to be fitted between $x = 0$ and $x = a$. So

$$n \cdot \frac{\lambda}{2} = a \implies \lambda = \frac{2a}{n}$$

whence

$$k = \frac{2\pi}{\lambda} = \frac{n\pi}{a}. \tag{1.36}$$

Only discrete choices of λ, or equivalently k, corresponding to integer n are permitted. Only certain waves are possible. In fitting waves into this interval with its boundary conditions, we have our first encounter with what we later see is quantisation!

Qualitative understanding of functions

We shall meet equations we cannot solve exactly. For instance, they can involve transcendental functions such as trigonometric and exponential functions. However, a deep understanding of the behaviour of quantum systems emerges from plotting the functions, as well as from using calculus and a knowledge of their asymptotes and zeros. For instance Fig. 1.10 shows the two functions $y = \sqrt{x}$ and $y = \tan(x^2)$. Explain the behaviour

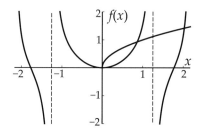

Figure 1.10: A plot of the functions $\sqrt{x}$ and $\tan(x^2)$.

of each function at important points such as the origin and at nodes (zeros) of the somewhat unusual tangent function. Why at one node is the slope zero, and why is it finite at others? Where are the nodes in general? Where the two functions cross are the solutions of the equation $\tan(x^2) = \sqrt{x}$.

Exercise 1.23: Plot the functions $y = \sqrt{x_0 - x}$ and $\tan(\sqrt{x})$ on the same graph for positive x, taking the former function up to x_0 (a constant). Identify the zeros and give their values and the behaviour of the functions around these zeros, in particular their slopes there. How many solutions does the equation $\tan(\sqrt{x}) = \sqrt{x_0 - x}$ possess. What about the equation $\tan(\sqrt{x}) = -\sqrt{x_0 - x}$? Similar analysis will be important for quantum wells of finite depth; see Sect. 3.1.

Hint: It might be helpful to differentiate or use the approximation that $\tan x \approx x$ for small x.

We later solve a slightly more complicated version of this problem to find the characteristic states of a quantum particle found in a finite square well; see Eq. (3.8).

A little calculus is sometimes helpful in analysing equations. Another transcendental equation is $e^x = kx$; see Fig. 1.11.

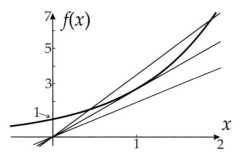

Figure 1.11: Plots of e^x, and of kx for various values of k.

Exercise 1.24: For what values of k do there exist solutions of the equation $e^x = kx$? What is the solution at the k, say k_c, where solutions first appear?

Hint: Consider the case where the line first touches the exponential. What two conditions are required there? Solve them simultaneously.

Exercise 1.25: Consider the equation $e^x = \frac{1}{2}ax^2$, for $a > 0$. For what ranges of a are there 1, 2, or 3 solutions to this equation?

It is very helpful to know the power series expansions of functions for small values of their arguments, and how in general to expand functions about an arbitrary point in their range. To get a first approximation recall that the derivative is the limiting ratio as $\delta x \to 0$

$$\frac{dy}{dx} \simeq \frac{\delta y}{\delta x} \simeq \frac{y(x_0 + \delta x) - y(x_0)}{\delta x}. \tag{1.37}$$

Rearranging we find that

$$y(x_0 + \delta x) \simeq y(x_0) + \delta x \cdot \left. \frac{dy}{dx} \right|_{x_0}, \tag{1.38}$$

so we have some knowledge of y at another point $(x_0 + \delta x)$ if we know $y(x_0)$ and the first derivative at x_0. We shall use a rearrangement of the first of Eq. (1.38) to get the difference of the values of a function evaluated at two different points: $y(x_0 + \delta x) - y(x_0) \simeq \delta x \cdot \frac{dy}{dx}$.

Repeated application of this procedure gives us better knowledge further away, at the expense of needing higher derivatives. So we may write in terms of derivatives evaluated at $x = x_0$, the *Taylor expansion*

$$y(x_0 + \delta x) = y(x_0) + \delta x \frac{dy}{dx} + \frac{(\delta x)^2}{2!} \frac{d^2y}{dx^2} + \frac{(\delta x)^3}{3!} \frac{d^3y}{dx^3} + \dots \qquad (1.39)$$

For instance, some familiar functions expanded about $x_0 = 0$ while calling δx simply x:

$$\sin(x) = x - \frac{x^3}{3!} + \frac{x^5}{5!} - \dots \qquad (1.40)$$

$$\cos(x) = 1 - \frac{x^2}{2!} + \frac{x^4}{4!} + \dots \qquad (1.41)$$

$$e^x = 1 + x + \frac{x^2}{2!} + \frac{x^3}{3!} + \dots \qquad (1.42)$$

$$\frac{1}{1-x} = 1 + x + x^2 + \dots \qquad (1.43)$$

$$\tan x = x + \frac{x^3}{3} + \frac{2x^5}{15} + \dots . \qquad (1.44)$$

Exercise 1.26: Confirm the expansions $(1 + x)^n = 1 + nx + \frac{n(n-1)}{2!}x^2 + \dots$ and $\tan(x) = x + x^3/3 + \dots$.
Hint: Recall that $\tan(x) = \sin(x)/\cos(x)$ and expand the denominator up into the numerator using (1.43) with a more complicated "x".

Exercise 1.27: For each of the functions in Eqns. (1.40–1.42), sketch the function, the separate terms in the approximation, and finally the sum of those terms on the same diagram.
Hint: Note how each successive term builds up to form a better approximation to the true function. There is an applet on our website which shows this dynamically.

Vectors

In Sect. 1.2 and Ex. 1.17, we analysed the downwards motion of a falling particle. Suppose we had fired the mass horizontally with speed v_0 at time $t = 0$. What is the subsequent motion of the mass? The horizontal and vertical motions are independent from each other. The vertical motion is as described previously. Since we have assumed no frictional forces, the horizontal speed remains constant.

Exercise 1.28: Show that the motion of the mass is parabolic with equation $y = (g/2v_0^2)x^2$, adopting the coordinates of Fig. 1.12.

The motion of the projectile is decoupled into horizontal and vertical directions, Newton's laws of course applying in both directions. However, we need not have chosen horizontal and vertical axes for Newton's laws to apply. We expect that the laws of physics are independent of our particular choice of co-ordinates. The mathematical way of expressing such laws is in terms of vectors.

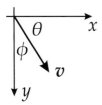

Figure 1.12: A vector v has magnitude and direction. It has an identity independent of a particular representation. It can be resolved into the x and y directions of a particular coordinate system.

A scalar quantity, such as the mass of the projectile, can be represented by a single number. A vector, such as velocity, by contrast possesses both magnitude and direction. The mass travels in a particular direction at a certain rate. We represent vectors in boldface or they are underlined in handwriting. Referred to a particular co-ordinate system, say, the usual x and y axes, the vector v of length v, has v_x and v_y components in x and y directions respectively,

$$v_x = v \cos \theta, \tag{1.45}$$

$$v_y = v \cos \phi, \tag{1.46}$$

where angles θ and ϕ are between v and the x and y axes respectively (see Fig. 1.12). Note that $\phi = \frac{\pi}{2} - \theta$. Written in components explicitly, v can be written as a row or column or numbers. Hence, we may write $v = (v_x, v_y)$ or $v = \begin{pmatrix} v_x \\ v_y \end{pmatrix}$. Squaring and adding the components, we find that

$$v_x^2 + v_y^2 = v^2 \cos^2 \theta + v^2 \cos^2 \phi$$
$$= v^2 (\cos^2 \theta + \sin^2 \theta) \tag{1.47}$$
$$= v^2$$

is independent of angle θ and thus of co-ordinate choice. Rotating our choice of axes does not change the length v of the vector; but it does change the components. It is the same object from different viewpoints.

More generally, the *scalar product* of vectors a and b, defined by

$$a \cdot b = a_x b_x + a_y b_y + a_z b_z, \tag{1.48}$$

is a co-ordinate independent scalar quantity. If $b = a$, then $a \cdot a = |a|^2 = a^2$ is called the modulus squared of vector a. The modulus is the length of the vector. An important scalar for our later work is that of the particle's kinetic energy $T = \frac{1}{2}mv \cdot v = \frac{1}{2}m(v_x^2 + v_y^2 + v_z^2)$. The meaning of this expression is that the kinetic energies in the different perpendicular directions add to give the total.

Exercise 1.29: Write the kinetic energy in terms of the components of the momentum p.

Exercise 1.30: By considering $c = a + b$ or otherwise, show that $a \cdot b$ is independent of the choice of co-ordinates.

Solution: Use the result that $|a|^2$, $|b|^2$ and $|c|^2$ are invariant upon co-ordinate rotation together with the definition of scalar product.

Exercise 1.31: By appropriate choice of axes or otherwise, show that

$$a \cdot b = ab \cos \theta, \tag{1.49}$$

where $\theta \in [0, \pi)$ is the angle between vectors a and b. If $a \cdot b = 0$ then a and b are perpendicular or *orthogonal* to each other. In general, the trigonometric factor $\cos \theta$ shows the dot product has the meaning of the projection of b along a times the length of a or equivalently *vice verse*. We use this in analysing 2-D waves in Sect. 5.3.

If the unit vectors[4] in the x, y and z directions are i, j and k respectively, then a vector can be written as

$$\begin{aligned} v &= v_x i + v_y j + v_z k \\ &= (v \cdot i)i + (v \cdot j)j + (v \cdot k)k, \end{aligned} \tag{1.50}$$

where we have made use of the result of Ex. 1.31. This way of expressing the vector is called resolving or expanding into basis vectors.

---

[4]Conventionally in vector analysis, these are denoted with a hat above the vector, e.g. $\hat{i}$. However, we shall reserve the hat for use with quantum mechanical operators.

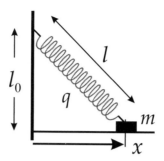

Figure 1.13: A constrained mass on a spring

1.3 Summary

To gain a deep understanding of physics, including quantum mechanics, one requires mathematical fluency. We have revised the essentials of probability, algebra and calculus, and derived results which will be used in later chapters, particularly those of the harmonic oscillator and waves on a string. More mathematical material and practice is in Chapter 4.1 where i, that is $\sqrt{-1}$, is introduced.

Quantum mechanics is founded on different physical concepts from classical physics. Central is the idea of a wavefunction from which we can derive the probability of finding a particle in a given position.

Adopting a theory based on probability, we found that it is impossible to determine simultaneously the position and momentum of particles beyond a certain accuracy (Heisenberg's uncertainty principle). We shall explore the ramifications of this in later chapters. To describe the motion of quantum particles, we use the idea of potential energy rather than forces. The classical potential problems we give are important practice for this new approach.

1.4 Additional problems

Exercise 1.32: A particle of energy $E_2 = 5V_0$ approaches the potential of Fig. 1.4. How long does it take to travel from $-a$ to $+2a$?

Exercise 1.33: A particle of mass m is constrained to slide along a smooth wire lying along the x axis, as shown in Figure 1.13. The particle is attached to a spring of natural length l_0 and spring constant q which has its other end fixed at $x = 0$, $y = l_0$.

(a) Obtain an expression for the force exerted on m in the x direction.

(b) For small displacements ($x \ll l_0$), how does the force depend upon displacement x?

(c) The potential $U(x)$ depends upon x in the form of $U \simeq Ax^n$ for small x. What are the values of n and A in terms of the constants given?

(d) Find the exact potential.

(e) By sketching a graph of the potential energy, suggest qualitatively how the period of oscillation of the object will depend on the amplitude.

(f) For $n = 4$ and amplitude x_0, show that the period is

$$\tau = 4 \frac{1}{x_0} \sqrt{\frac{m}{2A}} \int_0^1 \frac{du}{\sqrt{1 - u^4}}.$$

Exercise 1.34: An ideal spring obeying a linear force-extension law will store elastic potential energy when stretched or compressed. A real spring will often have other (smaller) force-extension terms included, and can be used as a model for the attractive and repulsive forces in other systems. In this example we add to the force a quadratic repulsive term, $q_2 x^2$, to the linear attractive term, the restoring force eventually becoming repulsive at large enough x values.

$$F(x) = -q_1 x + q_2 x^2.$$

(a) Calculate the potential energy, $U(x)$, stored in the spring for a displacement x. Take $U = 0$ at $x = 0$.

(b) It is found that the stored energy for $x = -a$ is twice the stored energy for $x = +a$. What is q_2 in terms of q_1 and a?

(c) Sketch the potential energy diagram for the spring.

(d) Consider a particle attached to the end of this spring. At what amplitude of motion in the $x > 0$ region does the particle cease to oscillate? At what $x < 0$ would we release the particle from rest in order to start seeing this failure to oscillate? Describe the motion.

Exercise 1.35: Functions ψ_0 and ψ_1 describing the first two quantum states of the harmonic oscillator are $\psi_0(u) = A_0 e^{-u^2/2}$ and $\psi_1(u) = A_1 2u e^{-u^2/2}$ where A_0 and A_1 are normalisations that ensure $\int_{-\infty}^{\infty} \psi^2 du = 1$. The variable u is related to the displacement from the minimum of the quadratic potential, see page 58. Show that $A_1 = A_0/\sqrt{2}$. Do not evaluate A_0, but give a value for the particle's mean square position when in the second quantum state: $\langle u^2 \rangle = \int_{-\infty}^{\infty} u^2 \psi_1^2 du$.

Exercise 1.36: Show that $\int_0^a x \sin^2(kx) dx = \frac{a^2}{4} \left[1 - \frac{\sin(2ka)}{ka} + \frac{\sin^2(ka)}{(ka)^2} \right]$.

2

Schrödinger's equation and potential wells.

The Schrödinger equation, operators, physical variables, a simple confining potential, quantisation, eigenstates, Sturm–Liouville theory

We see experimentally that particles exhibit wave-like phenomena such as diffraction and interference, and so there must be waves associated with them. We describe such waves by a wavefunction, $\psi(x)$, which we assume in turn specifies the particle, or a more general quantum system, entirely. Associated with this new description of particles is a new mathematical language for quantum phenomena.

2.1 Observables and operators

In physics we are concerned with physical or observable variables, the most important of which is the energy E of a particle. It is composed of the kinetic and potential energies denoted by $T(x)$ and $V(x)$ respectively. Other observables include for instance momentum, p, and position x. In quantum mechanics, corresponding to such measurable quantities are operators, which are denoted by a hat^on the relevant symbol, for instance $\hat{x}$, $\hat{p}$, $\hat{T}$, etc. In Chapter 4 we motivate how these operators are arrived at, guided by analogy with the quantum laws of radiation, but until then we concentrate mostly on the energy operators.

In the formulation of quantum mechanics which we shall discuss, the operators act on wavefunctions. An operator, $\hat{O}$, takes a function, say f, and produces from it, in general, another function, say g,

$$\hat{O}f = g. \tag{2.1}$$

It is analogous to a function: a function takes a number as an input and outputs another number. Operators are often differential operators or, sometimes, just the operation of multiplication by a function — we see concrete examples below. A simple example is where $\hat{O} = d/dx$ so that $\hat{O}f(x) = df/dx$. Thus $\hat{O}\sin(kx) = k\cos(kx)$, as in Eq. (1.13); Eqs. (1.14) and (1.15) provide two other important examples of the effect of this $\hat{O}$. It will turn out that this particular operator is closely related to momentum. An important feature of operator $\hat{O}$ is linearity. This means that

$$\hat{O}(af(x) + bg(x)) = a\hat{O}f(x) + b\hat{O}g(x), \tag{2.2}$$

for any numbers a and b, and any functions $f(x)$ and $g(x)$. In quantum mechanics we shall only be concerned with operators that are linear.

When the system is in a state with a well-defined value for that variable, the effect of the operator acting on the wavefunction ψ is to return the *same* ψ multiplied by that physical value for the variable; these are eigenfunctions and eigenvalues respectively (see below). For instance, $\hat{x}\psi(x) = x\psi(x)$, distinguishing between the operator (with the hat ^) and the observable value x of the position. This relation looks a little trivial because x, the spatial variable, is the same as the one chosen to base ψ on. An important operator is that of energy, $\hat{H}$, known as the *Hamiltonian*. So, the eigenvalue equation for energy is $\hat{H}\psi(x) = E\psi$, where E is observable energy of the wavefunction.

Since the total energy is the sum of kinetic and potential energies, $E = T + V$, the Hamiltonian operator is the sum of the kinetic and potential energy operators $\hat{H} = \hat{T} + \hat{V}$. Furthermore, the energy eigenvalue equation is written symbolically as

$$\boxed{\left(\hat{T}(x) + \hat{V}(x)\right)\psi(x) = E\psi(x),} \tag{2.3}$$

which is the Schrödinger equation. In this formulation of quantum mechanics, the kinetic energy is the differential operator $\hat{T} = -\frac{\hbar^2}{2m}\frac{d^2}{dx^2}$, which we will clearly later have to relate to the momentum operator since classically $T = p^2/2m$. The potential depends on position x, and its operator, $\hat{V}$, just produces the potential energy at the point x. In this formulation it returns the value $V(x)$; for simplicity of writing its hat will often be taken off in such energy relations as above. Using $\hat{T}$ in Eq. (2.3), the quantum wavefunction is governed by

$$\hat{H}\psi = -\frac{\hbar^2}{2m}\frac{d^2\psi}{dx^2} + V(x)\psi(x) = E\psi(x), \qquad (2.4)$$

a second order differential equation, which is known as the *time-independent Schrödinger equation*. For the moment we take Eq. (2.4) as a working assumption or postulate, along with the ideas that the system is described by the wavefunction ψ that emerges, and that the energy is given by the eigenvalue E corresponding to that emergent solution. See Chapter 4 for more on operators.

In regions where $V = V_0$, a constant, Eq. (2.4) rearranges to:

$$\frac{\hbar^2}{2m}\frac{d^2\psi}{dx^2} = -[E - V_0]\psi(x), \qquad (2.5)$$

an equation evidently with solutions either of the sinusoidal or of the exponential form depending on whether $E > V_0$ or $E < V_0$ respectively. See Chapter 1.2, especially the similarities with Eqs. (1.27). Other forms of the potential energy $V(x)$ are also important; $V(x) = \frac{1}{2}qx^2$ is the harmonic oscillator potential also discussed in the mathematical preliminaries. Other entities also execute harmonic oscillations in a generalised sense: for instance, a stretched string and the electromagnetic oscillations of space. The latter motion, in its quantised form, is the basis of Quantum Electrodynamics (QED), and in Sect. 5.3 we explicitly quantise the string. Another example is the Coulomb attractive potential between a nucleus and its satellite electrons a distance r apart: $V(r) = -e^2/(4\pi\epsilon_0 r)$ for a hydrogen atom, where e is the magnitude of the electronic charge. A periodic form of an electrostatic potential exists in metal and semiconductor crystals, giving the special quantum states of electrons that characterise metallic and semiconducting conductivity.

Eigenfunctions and eigenvalues

Generally in quantum mechanics we solve Sturm–Liouville type equations, see Sect. 2.3. These are of the form "operator", $\hat{H}$, acting on some function giving rise to the *same* function up to a multiplicative constant. That is $\hat{H}\psi = E\psi$. E is called the *eigenvalue*, which will be the result of measuring the physical observable associated with this operator. An equation with this property is commonly called an *eigen equation* after the German word eigen = "own" or "characteristic". Here the eigenvalue E is the characteristic energy, more frequently called the eigen energy.

Exercise 2.1: Write down the eigenfunctions and their associated eigenvalues for the operator $-\frac{d^2}{dx^2}$.

Exercise 2.2: Show that the operator $\hat{H} = \frac{d}{dx} + x$ has eigenfunctions of the form $y = \exp\left(ax - \frac{x^2}{2}\right)$. What are the associated eigenvalues?

Exercise 2.3: Consider the operator $\hat{L} = (1 - x^2)\frac{d^2}{dx^2} - 2x\frac{d}{dx}$ acting on the functions $y_1 = x$, $y_2 = \frac{1}{2}(3x^2 - 1)$ and $y_3 = \frac{1}{2}(5x^3 - 3x)$. Show that in each of these cases

$$\hat{L}y_n = -n(n+1)y_n, \qquad (2.6)$$

that is, $\hat{L}$ has the Sturm–Liouville property, with eigenvalues $-n(n+1)$. Further show that if $n \neq m$, then for $n, m = 1, 2, 3$:

$$\int_{-1}^{1} y_m(x)y_n(x)dx = 0. \qquad (2.7)$$

This property of functions under integration is called orthogonality (cf. orthogonal vectors in Ex. 1.31 and the discussion around Eq. (3.18), page 58).

These functions are in fact the Legendre polynomials, usually called $P_n(x)$ rather than $y_n(x)$. They describe states with well-defined angular momentum, including its projection along a particular axis.

Matrices analogously can be seen as operators, operating on vectors. They too have eigenvalues and eigenvectors. The use of such operators in quantum physics is the Heisenberg matrix mechanics approach[1] which is equivalent to the wavefunction and differential operator approach we adopt in this text. The parallel may help some readers who have met matrices before: a matrix $\underline{\underline{A}}$ (an operator) acts on vectors v to produce another vector u, that is $\underline{\underline{A}} \cdot v = u$. Of particular interest is where the new vector u is simply a multiple of the original one, that is $u = av$, so that the operator equation is $\underline{\underline{A}} \cdot v = av$, and is an eigen equation with eigenvalues a. In general the eigenvectors of $\underline{\underline{A}}$ are orthogonal, that is $v_i \cdot v_j = 0$ for different

---

[1]Described very briefly in §4.2.

eigenvectors v_i and v_j of $\underline{\underline{A}}$ (the analogue of Eq. (2.7) in the differential operator approach). Whatever types of operators are used to represent physical variables, the only possible result of a particular observation of this variable is one of the eigenvalues of the operator.

Table 2.1: Relations between classical and quantum concepts

Classical	Quantum
Physical variables: x, p, E, ...	Operators: $\hat{x}$, $\hat{p}$, $\hat{H}$, ...
	Wavefunctions: $\psi(x)$
Newton's laws: $F = ma$	Eigen equations: $\hat{H}\psi = E\psi$

2.2 Some postulates of quantum mechanics

After our introduction to the language of quantum mechanics, we can state some of the basic principles or postulates of the theory. These are akin to Newton's laws in classical mechanics. They cannot be derived, and the test of whether they are correct must rely fundamentally with experiment.

Postulate 1 The state of a quantum mechanical system is completely specified by a function $\psi(x, t)$ that is in general complex[2], and which depends on the position x of the particle and on time t. This function is called the wavefunction.

Postulate 2 The wavefunction has the property that $|\psi(x)|^2\, dx$ is the probability that the particle lies between x and $x + dx$. This assumes the wavefunction is normalised so that the total probability is unity: i.e. $\int |\psi(x)|^2\, dx = 1$.

Postulate 3 To every observable or measurable quantity A in classical mechanics, there corresponds a suitable linear operator $\hat{A}$ in quantum mechanics.

Postulate 4 The result of any measurement of observable A can only be one of the eigenvalues a of the associated operator $\hat{A}$, which satisfy the eigenvalue equation

$$\hat{A}\psi_a = a\psi_a,$$

---

[2]We explain complex numbers (with both real and imaginary parts) in Chapter 4. Until then, the wavefunctions we meet can be taken to be real without loss of generality.

where ψ_a is the eigenfunction of $\hat{A}$ corresponding to the eigenvalue a. Such eigenvalues are real.

The remainder of this text explores the consequences of these postulates and the intuition it offers about the quantum world. In Chapter 5, we shall introduce the remaining postulates and use them to understand how the wavefunction evolves with time.

2.3   The infinite square well potential

Figure 2.1:   An   infinite square well with the ground state and first excited state wavefunctions $\psi_1(x)$ and $\psi_2(x)$.   The forbidden regions (shaded) are $x \le 0$ and $x \ge a$.

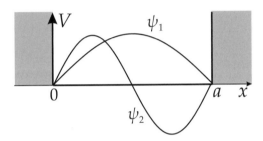

A simple, conceptually important example of quantum mechanics is confinement to an interval $0 < x < a$; see Fig. 2.1. The infinite square well potential that strictly localises particles in this way is $V = \infty$ for $x \le 0$ and $x \ge a$, and $V = 0$ inside the well. Schrödinger's equation in the well becomes

$$\frac{d^2\psi}{dx^2} = -\frac{2mE}{\hbar^2}\psi = -k^2\psi, \tag{2.8}$$

where $k = \sqrt{2mE}/\hbar$ has the units of inverse length. It is the same equation as for waves on a string, §1.2. The solutions are $\psi \propto \sin(kx)$ and $\psi \propto \cos(kx)$, and the general solution is $A\sin(kx) + B\cos(kx)$. We have the boundary conditions $\psi = 0$ at $x = 0$ and $x = a$, since the particle has zero probability of being outside the well where the potential is infinite. The first condition is assured by discarding the cosine solutions, since $\cos(0) = 1$ while $\sin(0) = 0$. The second condition then demands that the surviving solution vanishes at a, that is $\sin(ka) = 0$, which is only true for selected values k_n of k:

$$k_n a = n\pi;   n = 1,2,3,\ldots \tag{2.9}$$

With these choices of k we have fitted standing waves into the box, as it is said in physics. The requirements are exactly as for standing waves on a string, §1.2. The wavefunctions are accordingly $\psi_n(x) \propto \sin(k_n x)$. These quantised states are known as the *stationary states* of the system since they are solutions of the time-independent Schrödinger equation and determine the probability of finding the now quantised particle in various positions in the confining region. We shall discuss the time evolution of the wavefunction in Sect. 5.4.

Exercise 2.4: Sketch on top of Fig. 2.1 shapes of the probability distributions $P_n(x) \propto |\psi_n(x)|^2$ for a particle in its $n = 1$ and $n = 2$ states. Take care with the probability around its nodes (zeros).

Figure 2.1 shows that the width a must be an integer or half integer number of wavelengths. Equation (2.9) has $a = n\pi/k$ whence by identification of these two forms of a, we have $2\pi/k = \lambda$ as the wavelength, or $k = 2\pi/\lambda$ as the wavevector. Recall Sect. 1.2 where we viewed the argument kx of trigonometrical functions as an angle. We see now that this angle is $\theta = kx = 2\pi x/\lambda$, and can be thought of as a phase. This technique of fitting waves into a cavity arises also in blackbody radiation theory where the waves are electromagnetic, rather than particle waves, and are also quantised in this manner. Particles confined in only one spatial dimension could for instance be electrons confined between two plates of separation a and free to move in the other two dimensions. One can realise such confinement in the gate region of a transistor; see Fig. 2.5. We deal more precisely with the dimensionality of confining potentials in Sect. 5.3, where we explore modern examples such as electrons confined to a narrow path, a so-called nano-wire.

Exercise 2.5: The wavelength $\lambda = 2\pi/k = h/\sqrt{2mE}$ is the de Broglie wavelength of a particle; see Eq. (4.15). What is λ for (a) an electron having fallen through a potential of 1 volt, (b) a tennis ball of energy 1 joule?

Quantisation

Exercise 2.6: What are the energies of a particle of mass m in the infinite potential well of Fig. 2.1?

Solution: Since $E\psi = -\frac{\hbar^2}{2m}\frac{d^2\psi}{dx^2}$, then differentiating $\psi \propto \sin(kx)$ twice and cancelling the ψ on each side of the equation gives simply $E = \hbar^2 k^2/(2m)$.

There is a characteristic $k_n = n\pi/a$ for each n and therefore also a characteristic energy

$$E_n = \frac{\hbar^2 \pi^2 n^2}{2ma^2} = E_1 n^2. \tag{2.10}$$

for the nth state. The subscript on the k and the E are labels to remind us of which state we have. The ground state energy $E_1 = \frac{\hbar^2 \pi^2}{2ma^2}$ is characteristic of the well. The higher levels n are increasingly spaced as n^2.

We say that the system has been quantised (in effect by the imposition of boundary conditions[3]). Energy levels E_n and wavevectors k_n take discrete (eigen) values. The state $\psi_n \propto \sin(k_n x)$ is an eigenstate of the infinite square well. That states of a system, and the associated energies and other variables, are discrete is one of the deepest discoveries in all of physics — the notion of "quanta". The Schrödinger equation $(\hat{T} + V)\psi_n = E\psi_n$ is perhaps the most celebrated example of an eigen equation. It is of the special form discussed in Sect. 2.1, in that the operators on the left hand side act on ψ to produce (on the right hand side) a multiple of ψ itself. The operator $\hat{T} + V$ transforms ψ to itself only if ψ is an eigenstate and if E takes the value of the corresponding eigenvalue of $\hat{T} + V$.

Exercise 2.7: An eigenstate has wavefunction $\psi_n = A_n \sin(k_n x)$ in the interval $(0, a)$. Show that $A_n = \sqrt{2/a}$ in order to make the total probability unity in this state. The A factor is known as the normalisation.

Hint: Recall how ψ determines the probability density and what condition such a density must satisfy. A trigonometric double angle result will be required.

Exercise 2.8: Re-solve Ex. 2.7 for $V = 0$, $-a/2 < x < a/2$, with $V = \infty$ otherwise. Give explicit forms for the normalised eigenfunctions.

Kinetic energy and the wavefunction

Identification of eigenstates, Sturm–Liouville theory

Exercise 2.9: Draw the first few eigenstates of the infinite well problem. What do you notice about the extremes of curvature (second derivative)

---

[3]Discrete energy levels are a universal consequence of such boundary conditions.

and the number of nodes? For a given ψ_n, write down the explicit form of the wavefunction and calculate the curvature at these extremes.

Sketched on Fig. 2.1 we see what we now know to be ψ_1 and ψ_2, the ground and first excited states of the well. ψ starts from $x = 0$ with positive slope, developing a positive value. Thus from Eq. (2.8) in the form $d^2\psi/dx^2 = -k^2\psi$, it has a negative second derivative, that is downward curvature. Such bending down of ψ eventually makes it intersect the axis and give itself another node. For states other than the ground state (where this node is also the other end of the well), after the node ψ then becomes negative; when $\psi < 0$ the curvature $-k^2\psi$ is then positive and ψ bends up towards the next node from below; see Fig. 2.2. Generally, the curvature is proportional to the kinetic energy, $E - V = T$. The greater the curvature, the more rapidly ψ bends to achieve the next node and thus in a given interval more nodes will be achieved in states with higher energy.

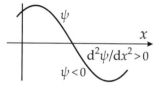

Figure 2.2: When kinetic energy $E - V(x)$ is positive the rate of change of slope of the wave function is opposite to its sign; ψ returns to the axis and overshoots, producing nodes.

The result is generic and is an aspect of the Sturm–Liouville theory of differential equations: the eigenstates of appropriate operator equations (including Schrödinger's) have real eigenvalues which, moreover, can be enumerated in increasing order, starting with a lowest eigenvalue, by counting the nodes of the corresponding eigenfunctions. Thus here ψ_1 has 0 nodes (not counting the end point nodes which are inflicted by the infinite potential), ψ_2 has 1, and so on. One could perhaps have labelled the ground state ψ_0, which is sometimes done, for instance in the quantum mechanics of oscillators (Sect. 3.2). We shall use this theory to identify and understand the eigenstates of more complicated potentials. Eigenvalues being real is essential since physical quantities, such as energy, arise as eigenvalues of their corresponding operator equations and, of course, are real.

2.4 Confinement energy revisited

Recall that the Heisenberg uncertainty principle gave a $p \sim \hbar/\Delta x$, where $\sim$ means "of the general order of", and hence in Eq. (1.2) a confinement kinetic energy of $T = p^2/2m \propto \hbar^2/(2m(\Delta x)^2)$. (Explain why we have been able to replace Δp by p.) Thus spatial confinement leads to an energy due to the associated momentum that localisation generates. An explicit calculation for the infinite well has given an energy $T_n = E_n = \hbar^2 \pi^2 n^2 / (2ma^2)$ of confinement. We can also calculate explicitly what the confinement is for each state:

Exercise 2.10: Show that for the nth eigenstate of the infinite well, the variance in position is $a^2 \left(\frac{1}{12} - \frac{1}{2\pi^2 n^2} \right)$. Note that the limit $n \to \infty$ of this formula is $a^2/12$, which you should show is the variance for the classical distribution of a particle in an infinite well. The tending of quantum averages to their classical counterparts in the limit of high eigenstates is called the *Correspondence Principle*.

Hint: See Ex. 1.7 for the key result on variance. One needs to integrate by parts (twice) and repeatedly use values for $\cos(2k_n a)$ and $\sin(2k_n a)$; see also Ex. 1.15. Classically particles would be uniformly distributed through the well.

The uncertainty in position, that is Δx, is the square root of this variance.

Exercise 2.11: A parallel beam of neutrons with speed $200\,\mathrm{m\,s^{-1}}$ is incident on an absorbing sheet with a slit of width 0.01 mm. Calculate the width of the beam 10 m behind the slit.

Hint: The slit localises the neutrons transversely (y) to their propagation direction, x. The resulting Δp_y gives a range of sideways motions, associated with the y uncertainty, superimposed on the x-motion.

Heisenberg meets Coulomb

The structure of atoms

The energy of an electron in the attractive electric field of a nucleus of charge Ze is $V(r) = -Ze^2 / (4\pi\epsilon_0 r)$ where r is the particles' separation, e is the electronic charge and ϵ_0 is the permittivity of free space; see page 5 for the Coulomb potential. One can wonder why the electron does not simply disappear into the nucleus ($r \to 0$) to indefinitely lower its energy[4]. The

---

[4]There are other problems such as any orbital motion of a classical type would involve centripetal acceleration and hence also, by classical electrodynamics, the emission of radiation. Electrons would then lose their energy and collapse into the nucleus. This second problem is also solved by quantum mechanics.

answer is the quantum mechanical kinetic energy $+\hbar^2/(2mr^2)$ arising from localisation to within r of the nucleus. This cost gives rise to the structure of atoms and molecules. Qualitatively, the total electronic energy when the electron is confined to within r is the sum of the confinement kinetic energy and the attractive (negative) electrical attraction to the proton, that is:

$$E = \frac{\hbar^2}{2mr^2} - \frac{Ze^2}{4\pi\epsilon_0 r}. \tag{2.11}$$

The minimum of E, at $dE/dr = 0$, gives the characteristic size

$$a_B = \frac{4\pi\epsilon_0\hbar^2}{me^2} = 53 \times 10^{-12} \text{ m} \tag{2.12}$$

$$a_Z = a_B/Z. \tag{2.13}$$

This length where quantum and electric (Coulomb) effects balance is the *Bohr radius*, a_B; see Fig. 2.3. It is the size of a hydrogen atom and is the fundamental atomic length scale. Remarkably, this expression for a_B is exact,

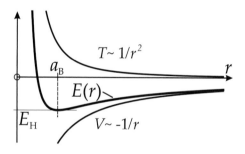

Figure 2.3: Electric attraction $(-1/r)$ and quantum repulsion $(1/r^2)$ compete in a hydrogen atom. The latter dominates at small r, and the former at large r. Overall, their sum (heavy line) has a minimum with negative energy, E_H, at the Bohr radius.

despite it arising from a simple qualitative argument. A full description demands the solution of Eq. (2.4) with $V(r) = -e^2/(4\pi\epsilon_0 r)$ and in three dimensions. See Exs. 5.1 & 5.2 for more illustration of this $V(r)$, whilst Ex. 3.19 explores the hydrogenic ground state wavefunction. The exactness of numerical factors in our result is accidental. However, the argument leading from Eq. (2.11) to (2.12) gives the correct *scaling* with $\epsilon_0, \hbar, m$ and e; that is, the relevant fundamental quantities occur in the right combination.

Exercise 2.12: Using the simple minimisation argument, show that the binding energy required to separate the proton and electron of the H atom is

$$E_H = -\frac{1}{2}\frac{me^4}{(4\pi\epsilon_0)^2\hbar^2}. \tag{2.14}$$

By exploring this combination of fundamental constants of nature, show
that $E_H = -13.6$ eV.

The electron volt, eV, is the energy released when an electron drops
through a 1 V potential difference: 1 eV $=1.6 \times 10^{-19}$ J. The $-$ sign says the
electron is bound to the proton. The ionisation energy to remove the e^- to
create an H^+ ion (proton) is 13.6 eV.

Because molecules are larger than H atoms, or because one is dealing
with the transfer only of outer electrons between species, the energy scale
of chemistry is somewhat lower, $\lesssim 1$ eV. For instance batteries working
on the chemistry of e.g. Zn, Ni, Pb, Li etc. deliver charge at a potential of
about 1 V. Check that the energy hc/λ for photons with wavelength λ in the
visible part of the electromagnetic spectrum ($\lambda \sim 500$ nm) is in this range.

Einstein meets Heisenberg and Coulomb

Relativity intrudes into quantum mechanics

What happens when the localisation energy reaches relativistic values?
Recall the Einstein mass–energy equivalence $E = mc^2$, where m is the particle mass and c the speed of light. If in the $n = 1$ quantum state we have confinement energy $\frac{\hbar^2 \pi^2}{2ma^2} = 2mc^2$, then we are dealing with energies sufficient
to create $e^+ + e^-$, an electron-positron pair, from the vacuum[5]. Rearranging, the confinement length scale for pair production to occur in this model
is $a = \frac{\pi}{2} \frac{\hbar}{mc}$. Ignoring the π and other factors, this fundamental length scale
where quantum mechanics meets relativity is

$$\lambda_C = h/mc = 2.4 \times 10^{-12} \text{ m}, \qquad (2.15)$$

the Compton wavelength (where $h = 2\pi\hbar$). The reduced Compton wavelength $\lambda_C/2\pi = \hbar/mc$ is the natural scale throughout relativistic quantum
mechanics.

Exercise 2.13: Show that the binding energy for an electron to a nucleus
with charge Z is $E_Z = -\frac{1}{2} \frac{me^4 Z^2}{(4\pi\epsilon_0)^2 \hbar^2}$. Compare the corresponding Bohr radius with the reduced Compton wavelength. At what Z does the atomic
confinement of an inner electron induce pair production from the vacuum?

---

[5]It is necessary to create particle-anti-particle *pairs* otherwise charge and other physical
quantities would not be conserved.

By comparing E_Z with $2mc^2$, the cost of creating a particle-anti-particle pair, confirm your estimate of nuclear stability. In effect the very intense electric field close to a large charge is polarising the vacuum to the point where it is unstable to particle production.

Hint: The critical atomic number from the Coulomb attractive energy plus the localisation repulsive energy emerges as $Z_c \sim 270$. The actual threshold for positron production is about 160, considering relativistic quantum effects and the finite size of the nucleus.

Experimentally, high nuclear charge atoms with atomic number $Z \geq 160$ arise as the, only briefly stable, fruits of e.g. two $Z \geq 80$ nuclei colliding with each other. The radii of the atomic orbitals of the inner electrons of the resultant nuclei become very small, falling below λ_c. The binding energy, E_Z, released by an electron falling into this Bohr state exceeds $2mc^2$. The vacuum is thereby induced to produce e^+e^- pairs. These are visible through the shower of e^+ (positrons) that emerge, while the partner e^- from pair production is retained to reduce the nuclei to a lower Z state. Quantum electrodynamics is quantum mechanics where the number of particles is variable due to these relativistic effects. It is the invention of Dirac, Schwinger, Feynman and others, and is one of mankind's supreme achievements; it is beyond the scope of this text[6].

Mass effects in localisation

The meeting of molecular and nuclear physics

Notice that the localisation kinetic energy scales like $T \propto \hbar^2 / mr^2$. We have seen the effect of changing r by various means, essentially electric (changing the nuclear charge Z). The fundamental constant $\hbar$ cannot be changed of course, though we can speculate as to how the world would be if $\hbar$ were to be large enough to bring quantum effects to the length and energy scales that we experience in the everyday world[7].

However, we can change the mass of the electron by considering instead its close relative, the muon, sometimes denoted by μ, which is like an electron but with larger mass, $m_\mu = 207m_e$.

---

[6]See "QED: The strange theory of light and matter" by R.P. Feynman, Penguin, 1985.

[7]"The new world of Mr Tompkins", George Gamow; edited by Russell Stanard in new paperback, CUP, 1999

Exercise 2.14: What is the Bohr radius for "muonium", that is the p—μ analogue of the H atom where instead a muon is bound to a proton?

The H_2^+ ion is two protons held together by attraction to a single electron; see the somewhat classical picture of Fig. 2.4.

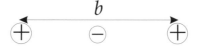

Figure 2.4: The H_2^+ molecular ion. Two protons are bound by a chemical bond consisting of a single electron largely localised between these sources of positive charge. The bond length is $b \sim 1.1 \times 10^{-10}$ m. It is the simplest molecular species.

Exercise 2.15: Consider the H_2^+ ion classically. Find the overall negative Coulomb energy (i.e. binding) when the (positive) protons are r apart and the (negative) electron is midway between them, Fig. 2.4. Discuss the stability of this arrangement of charges. How does quantum mechanics change your stability argument? Repeat the argument of the form in (2.11) and (2.12) to derive an expression for the bond length b.

Hint: Look up the mass ratio between protons and electrons and discuss why we can consider the protons as particles a definite distance apart. What localisation energies would the protons have when confined to the scale b?

The accident of exactness in the Bohr radius calculation does not occur here; compare your answer to the exact answer given in Fig. 2.4. However, the scaling that arises is correct and allows a precise answer to the following problem:

Exercise 2.16: If the electron in the H_2^+ ion is replaced by a muon, what is the new length of the chemical bond between the protons in terms of b for the conventional H_2^+ ion? What differences to your calculation arise if the protons are replaced by deuterons, that is hydrogen nuclei but with atomic mass 2 because the proton is accompanied by a neutron?

Hint: How do the localisation energies of the protons considered in the above exercise change when we further double the nuclear mass?

It turns out that the muon mediated D_2^+ molecular bond length is close to the length for the two deuterons to approach each other to fuse to form a heavier nucleus under the attractions of the strong nuclear force. In fact the deuterons quantum mechanically tunnel through a remaining region of electrostatic repulsion where they should not be found classically. In the next chapter we deal with presence of particles in "classically forbidden regions". Such fusion reactions in light nuclei release huge amounts of energy since the mass of the products is lower than that of the reactants. This so-called mass deficit Δm releases an energy of $(\Delta m)c^2$ (the Einstein mass-energy equivalence). The D-D chemical bond has become so short it is catalysing a nuclear reaction. When the energy is released the simple molecule falls apart and the muon is free to bind to other deuterons to form a new molecule and then to repeat the process of forming a short chemical bond and leading to nuclear fusion. In fact rates are faster for deuterium-tritium fusion and also the muon moves more freely subsequently to continue catalysis. (Tritium is the isotope of hydrogen with 1 proton and 2 neutrons.) The D-T catalytic nuclear fusion scheme almost works in a continuing manner! Unfortunately muons have a half life of only about 1 microsecond and are not long enough lived to catalyse enough reactions to yield overall more energy than the production of the muon costs[8].

Observation of quantum effects

We have seen in infinite wells, atoms and molecules the interplay between a confining potential and quantum mechanical resistance to localisation. It leads to quantum states with discrete energies that we have calculated in the 1-D square well case where they scale with the square of the quantum number, that is $E_n = E_1 n^2$. For hydrogen atoms we have calculated only the ground state energy and spatial extent, but there also exists a discrete spectrum of excited states above the ground state. Because H atoms are three-dimensional and the Coulomb potential gets weaker with distance from the proton, the excited state energies turn out to scale as $E_n = E_H/n^2$ rather. Recall that $E_H = -13.6$ eV.

Since they are charged, electrons interact strongly with electromagnetic radiation (micro-wave, infrared, visible, UV, X-ray, ..., light). When they

---

[8]Einstein and Coulomb can also meet classically. When $e^2/(4\pi\epsilon_0 r) = mc^2$ (conventionally there is no factor of 2 in the rest energy here), another length, the classical radius of the electron, $r_c = 2.8 \times 10^{-15}$ m emerges. Note however the electron is a point-like particle, though it does undergo relativistic oscillations (Zitterbewegung is German for shivering motion) of amplitude of order r_c.

are confined, their quantum transitions are easy to detect as emission or
absorption of discrete light quanta that convey the energy. Energy transfer from and to atoms, and other "wells" containing electrons, takes discrete values corresponding to the difference in energy of the levels between
which the electrons make transitions. These quanta of light are photons.
See Fig. 2.5(a) for an example of transitions between the levels of the infinite square well.

Figure 2.5: (a) The first
3 levels of an infinite
square well with an elec-
tron gaining or losing
energy (via photons)
to make transitions
between levels. (b) A
slab of semiconductor
of thickness a in the x
direction and of very
large extent in the y and
z directions.

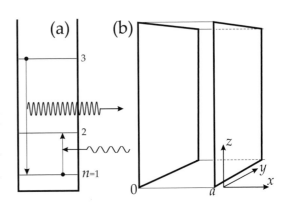

How can one realise the infinite square well of Sect. 2.3 and Ex. 2.6?
The kinetic energy arises because the particle is confined in one spatial direction, x. If it moves freely in the other two directions, then there is no
associated quantum mechanical confinement energy. Nano fabrication of
semiconducting slabs of thickness a in one direction, and large extent in the
other two, provides us with close models of the 1-D infinite square well if
the space outside the slab is vacuum, or filled with highly insulating oxide
layers for which an electron lacks the energy to penetrate; see Fig. 2.5(b).
Confinement additionally in more dimensions is dealt with in Chapter 5.3
— nano-wires and quantum dots. The light emitted or absorbed by these
structures tells us about their spatial extent and geometry. At the nano-
scale, quantum mechanics intrudes heavily into electronics:

Exercise 2.17: An electron is in a 1-D box, as in Fig. 2.5(b), of length $a = 1$
nm. Find in electron volts the energy of the ground state and of the next
two energy levels. Find the wavelength of the possible photons emitted or
absorbed during transitions between these states.

Hint: See Eqs. (4.12)–(4.13) for the connections between E, k and λ for photons.

2.5 Summary

Chapter 2 introduced the postulates of quantum mechanics. These are the fundamental laws governing the theory. Physical observables of classical mechanics are replaced by operators which act on wavefunctions. Measurements of the system correspond to obtaining eigenvalues of the eigenvalue equation for the operator/observable. The most important eigenvalue operator is that for the energy — the time independent Schrödinger equation

$$-\frac{\hbar^2}{2m}\frac{d^2\psi(x)}{dx^2} + V(x)\psi(x) = E\psi(x).$$

Our first application of the Schrödinger equation was the infinite square well. The solutions resemble those of waves on a stretched string though the interpretation is completely different. Confining the matter waves inside a box (via boundary conditions) leads to only certain allowable energy levels — quantisation.

The infinite square well demonstrates consistency with the uncertainty principle. We use Heisenberg's principle to deduce the sizes of atoms, where there is interplay between the kinetic energy of confinement and the potential energy of the confining potential. We have also seen its role in understanding vacuum polarisation around heavy nuclei and muon catalysed fusion.

2.6 Additional problems

Exercise 2.18: A particle in a 1-D box of length a is in its ground state. What is the probability of finding it (a) in the region $a/4 < x < 3a/4$, (b) in a very small interval Δx centred at $x = a/2$, (c) in an interval Δx at a wall. Repeat for when it is in its first excited state.

3

Entering classically forbidden regions

Negative kinetic energy, penetration of potentials, joining wavefunctions, finite square wells, quantum oscillators

After the infinite square well, the next simplest problem is the finite square well, where we relax the height of the barrier. Many features of the infinite well remain, such as sinusoidal wavefunctions inside the well and a discrete set of allowable energy levels. However, we now have the possibility of the particle being found outside the well, where the particle would classically have negative kinetic energy. Using the physics gained from the finite well, we then consider the most important potential in physics: the harmonic oscillator. The harmonic oscillator has wide ranging applications including the quantisation of the electromagnetic field.

3.1 The finite square well potential

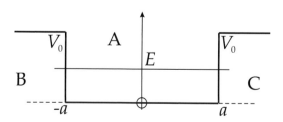

Figure 3.1: A finite well of depth V_0 and width $2a$. Region A is classically allowed, while B and C are classically forbidden for particles with energy $E < V_0$.

Consider the finite square well potential of Fig. 3.1 with width $2a$ and depth V_0, that is $V = 0$ for $-a < x < a$ and $V = V_0$ otherwise. A particle with total energy $E < V_0$ is bound since classically it has too little energy to rise out of the well; in fact its kinetic energy $E - V_0$ would be negative when outside the well. By contrast, see Ex. 4.24 for a free particle, that is one with enough kinetic energy to rise out of the well. Were the bound particle classical, it would be strictly localised by the potential to the region of $-a < x < a$ which is termed the classically allowed region, A. Its probability of being found at x in this interval would be $P(x) = 1/(2a)$, and $P(x) = 0$ otherwise. The particle has positive kinetic energy $T = E > 0$ in this classically allowed region. Note that we measure energies E and V_0 with respect to the bottom of the well. Potentials which have a dipped or well shape to them, are termed *attractive* because of the possibility for particles to be bounded or trapped inside the potential.

We now see how a quantum particle can leave the classical domain. The Schrödinger equation in the regions A, and in B or C is

Region A:
$$\frac{\hbar^2}{2m} \frac{d^2\psi}{dx^2} = -E\psi \tag{3.1}$$

Regions B/C:
$$\frac{\hbar^2}{2m} \frac{d^2\psi}{dx^2} = +(V_0 - E)\psi. \tag{3.2}$$

We are dealing with *one* equation, but where its form changes piecewise from region to region. The first form, in A, is that of SHM that we have met before: $d^2\psi/dx^2 = -k^2\psi$ with solutions

$$\psi_A \propto \sin(kx) \text{ or } \psi_A \propto \cos(kx), \tag{3.3}$$

where $k = \sqrt{2mE}/\hbar$. The second form, relevant for B or C where the kinetic energy $E - V_0 < 0$ is negative, is qualitatively different with solutions

$$\begin{cases} \psi_B \propto e^{+k'x} & \text{for } -\infty < x < -a \\ \psi_C \propto e^{-k'x} & \text{for } a < x < \infty. \end{cases} \tag{3.4}$$

The wavevector $k' = \sqrt{2m(V_0 - E)}/\hbar$ is no longer associated with oscillations of ψ, but instead with exponential decay. In going from A to B/C in (3.3) to (3.4) we go from positive to negative kinetic energy. Note that both $e^{\pm k'x}$ are solutions to Eq. (3.2) and we have taken that solution which decays to zero a long way away from the well (evanescent solution).

Matching wavefunctions

One needs to know how to wed together the three different solutions at the boundaries of the different regions.

The requirements for wavefunction matching are

(i) the wavefunction ψ must be continuous, and

(ii) the derivative $d\psi/dx$ must be continuous everywhere.

Both requirements pertain where the functional form of ψ abruptly changes, for instance here at the points $x = \pm a$. Condition (ii) is not true at points of the potential that are pathological, e.g. where $V \to \infty$ at the edges of the infinite square well potential; see Ex. 3.20 where the requirements are simply derived.

The quantum states of the finite well

We can now solve the finite square well potential: let the solutions be

$$\psi_A = A\cos(kx); \quad \psi_B = Be^{k'x}; \quad \psi_C = Ce^{-k'x}. \tag{3.5}$$

Conditions (i) and (ii) for wavefunction matching at $x = a$ yield

(i) $$A\cos(ka) = Ce^{-k'a} \tag{3.6}$$

(ii) $$-Ak\sin(ka) = -Ck'e^{-k'a}. \tag{3.7}$$

These are two conditions that connect the magnitudes A and C of the wavefunctions and cannot be consistent with each other, except for special values of k and k'. Readers will now be (correctly) anticipating quantisation! Dividing (3.7) by (3.6) gives

$$\tan(ka) = k'/k$$

$$\Rightarrow \qquad \tan\left(\frac{a\sqrt{2m}}{\hbar}\sqrt{E}\right) = \sqrt{\frac{V_0}{E} - 1}. \tag{3.8}$$

See below Eq. (3.2) for k and k'. This transcendental equation holds only for particular values of E, and hence also for k, and we again find eigen energies (the energy levels) for which the states of a system exist. Equation (3.8) is the equivalent of condition (2.9) on k for the infinite well.

We cannot solve Eq. (3.8) exactly (but quite simply numerically). Revisit Fig. 1.10 and Ex. 1.23; we can understand much by drawing graphs. But first we rearrange Eq. (3.8) to a more universal and revealing dimensionless form, a procedure followed widely in physical analysis since it exposes the underlying scales such as those of length and energy. The argument of the tan will be rearranged to $\sqrt{E/E_W}$ where $E_W = \hbar^2/(2ma^2)$. Thus energies E and V_0 are reduced by the kinetic energy of localisation E_W, that is energies are expressed in new units of E_W. Subscript $_W$ stands for well, and E_W is effectively a measure of the well's half width a. We call $\epsilon = E/E_W$ the *reduced* energy. It is dimensionless[1]. Then Eq. (3.8) becomes

$$\tan\left(\sqrt{\epsilon}\right) = \sqrt{\frac{V_0/E_W}{\epsilon} - 1}, \qquad (3.9)$$

the solutions of which are the (reduced) eigen energies $\epsilon_1, \epsilon_2, \ldots$. They depend only on the single quantity, the reduced well depth V_0/E_W, that enters as a parameter in Eq. (3.9). This ratio is a measure of how deep the well is in relation to the quantum energies generated by its localising width; V_0 and E_W do not enter separately. Alternatively, one can view this as measuring the well depth in units of E_W, which are the natural choice in this problem. See Fig. 3.2 for a plot of the two sides of the equation. The

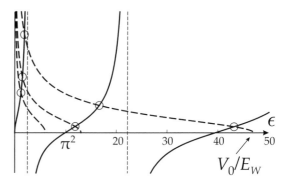

Figure 3.2: Dashed lines are $\sqrt{(V_0/E_W)/\epsilon - 1}$ for $V_0/E_W = 6, 13, 47$. The solid lines are $\tan(\sqrt{\epsilon})$. Their crossings (circled) are the solutions for the reduced eigen energies ϵ_i.

function $\sqrt{(V_0/E_W)/\epsilon - 1}$ on the right hand side of Eq. (3.9) diverges as $\epsilon \to 0$, and goes to zero (as a square root and therefore with infinite slope) at $\epsilon \to V_0/E_W$. Evidently the number of solutions (ringed on the graph) for ϵ depends on the reduced well depth V_0/E_W. There is always one solution, even for arbitrarily shallow wells; for $V_0/E_W > \pi^2$ there are more solutions. The solutions $E_n = \epsilon_n E_W$ are the bound states of the potential (eigenstates). The solutions for this kind of potential are qualitatively different from, say,

---

[1]Reduced variables give an equation generality — it can be applied to all equivalent situations and offers deeper insight. See the additional exercise 3.17.

the electronic states of an atom where infinitely many exist (a ground or lowest state, plus the excited states). One reason for the difference is that the Coulomb potential ($\propto 1/r$) is of infinite range. Another difference is that atoms are in 3-D.

Exercise 3.1: In what sense in the above is the well shallow?

Solution: By itself, the term shallow V_0 has little meaning since a comparison is invited with something of the same dimensions (energy). The only candidate is E_W. When V_0 is sufficiently small compared with E_W that only one bound state exists, its effect can perhaps be said to be minimal, that is, it is shallow. The condition for only one state is $V_0 < \hbar^2\pi^2/(2ma^2) \equiv \pi^2 E_W$. The energy $E_1 = \hbar^2\pi^2/(2ma^2)$ is the quantum localisation cost in the ground state of an infinite well of width a; see Ex. 2.6 and Eq. (2.10).

One might ask why, if a well becomes narrow or shallow so that the localisation kinetic energy is comparable to the well depth, the particle is not driven out of the well by this quantum mechanical cost? The answer is that the particle *is* in fact mostly outside the well! It is largely in the classically forbidden regions B and C, but it is still bound; see ψ_1 for $V_0/E_W = 0.5$ in Fig. 3.3.

We can sketch ψ for the ground and second excited states, and see qualitatively how the even states look; Fig. 3.3. There are no nodes for the

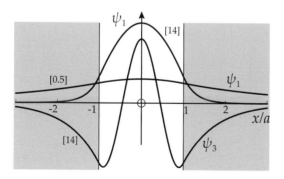

Figure 3.3: The eigenfunctions ψ_1 and ψ_3 for $V_0/E_W = 14$, and ψ_1 for $V_0/E_W = 0.5$. The classically forbidden region is grey. ψ_3 especially shows the change over from oscillation to decay.

ground state, as demanded by Sturm–Liouville theory. The central part of the wavefunction is a section of a cosine function which, for the next even excited state ψ_3 has space in which to oscillate and there are then two nodes in the classically allowed region.

Exercise 3.2: Confirm by calculation that the minima in ψ_3 occur in the allowed rather than in the classically forbidden regimes. Why *must* this be the case? (Think of negative versus positive kinetic energies.)

We have missed the states with an odd number 1, 3, 5 ... of nodes and Sturm–Liouville theory says that these states, the first, third, ... excited states, must interleave in energy with those that we have found. We made the choice $\cos(kx)$ in region A. Taking instead $\sin(kx)$ in A, an equally valid solution of Schrödinger's equation, gives us the odd set of eigenstates with an odd number of nodes.

Exercise 3.3: Repeat the above analysis for the odd energy eigenstates of the finite potential well. Be sure to sketch the wavefunctions and derive the transcendental equation to be solved for the eigen energies. Explore the solutions qualitatively as before. Show that there are no longer odd eigenstate for sufficiently small well depths.

Working through Ex. 3.1 showed that the lowest energy even eigenfunction survives as the well depth decreases, even if the odd states are eventually all lost. The survival of one state is an aspect of being in 1-D. By fitting suitable square wells inside arbitrary potentials, one can prove that *any* attractive potential in 1-D retains at least one bound state. In 3-D, when wells are sufficiently shallow, all the bound states can be lost; see Ex. 5.15 and discussion.

Note that the states of the well have a definite spatial symmetry about $x = 0$, either even ($\psi_1, \psi_3, \dots$) or odd ($\psi_2, \psi_4, \dots$).

Exercise 3.4: Show for a symmetric potential, for which $V(x) = V(-x)$, that the associated wavefunctions must be even or odd.

The even or oddness of $\psi(x)$ is known as its parity. Parity is of enormous significance in quantum physics.

3.2   The harmonic potential well

The next simplest confinement is that by the harmonic potential energy, $V(x) = \frac{1}{2}qx^2$, which increases quadratically about $x = 0$. As for infinite wells, particles are bound by the potential for all energies but, as in finite wells, particles can penetrate into classically forbidden regions. Harmonic potentials appear in many guises throughout physics. For instance, in a diatomic molecule, the atoms sit a characteristic distance r_0 apart under the influence of attractive and repulsive potentials. The minimum of the sum of these energies defines the bond length r_0. At a point r, the energy rises to $V(r) = \frac{1}{2}q(r - r_0)^2$, provided the excursion from the minimum is not too great. Since atoms are light, the quantised motion in such a potential is pronounced, and easily detectable by electromagnetic waves if the atoms are not identical.

The classical harmonic oscillator

A classical example of simple harmonic motion is that of a particle tethered by a spring, as discussed on page 18. The force f is minus the gradient of the potential and acts to restore the particle to the origin $x = 0$. Thus $f = -dV/dx = -qx$ (see Fig 3.4) and is oppositely directed to the displacement x — oscillations ensue when the particle is set in motion. [q is the spring constant, later referred to as the "well stiffness".]

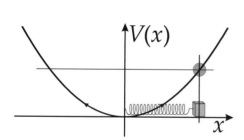

Figure 3.4: A harmonic (Hookean) spring displaced x from equilibrium position providing a restoring potential $V(x)$ to a mass. At the mass's current position the extent to which it has ridden up the potential is shown by the filled circle.

The differential equation of motion is hence (see Sect. 1.2)

$$m\frac{d^2x}{dt^2} = -qx \quad \Rightarrow \quad \frac{d^2x}{dt^2} = -\frac{q}{m}x \equiv -\omega^2x, \qquad (3.10)$$

where $\omega = \sqrt{q/m}$ is the angular frequency; see under Eq. (1.28) on page 19 for a definition of ω.

Exercise 3.5: Check by substitution that the general solution of the differential equation (3.10) is of the form $x(t) = x_s \sin(\omega t) + x_c \cos(\omega t)$, see Eq. (1.28), where x_s and x_c are two arbitrary constants that can be fixed from the boundary conditions.

Exercise 3.6: What is the speed of the particle above when its displacement is equal to half its amplitude, x_{osc}, of oscillation? Show generally that for SHM, its velocity is $v(x) = \pm\omega\sqrt{x_{osc}^2 - x^2}$.

Exercise 3.7: *What is the probability $P_{cl}(x)$ of finding a classical simple harmonic oscillator at position x? It will be instructive to compare this result with that found in the quantum case.

The quantum harmonic oscillator

The Schrödinger equation for the quantum harmonic oscillator, is upon, re-writing $V(x) = \frac{1}{2}m\omega^2x^2$,

$$-\frac{\hbar^2}{2m}\frac{d^2\psi}{dx^2} + \frac{1}{2}m\omega^2x^2\psi = E\psi. \tag{3.11}$$

As a solution, we require a ψ which when twice differentiated will have a part $\propto x^2\psi$ and another part $\propto \psi$ so that cancellation of the derivative term with $V\psi$ and $E\psi$ occurs and Eq.(3.11) can hold. Such a function is the Gaussian, written in its general form $\psi = A_0e^{-x^2/2\sigma^2}$, the $_0$ on the normalisation A anticipating that this will be the ground state[2]. Differentiating gives $\frac{d\psi}{dx} = -A_0\frac{x}{\sigma^2}e^{-x^2/2\sigma^2}$ and the second differentiation attacks the x factors in two places, giving $\frac{d^2\psi}{dx^2} = A_0\left(\frac{x^2}{\sigma^4} - \frac{1}{\sigma^2}\right)e^{-x^2/2\sigma^2}$. Returning these results to (3.11) yields

$$E\,\psi = \frac{1}{2}m\omega^2\,x^2\psi - \overbrace{\underbrace{\frac{\hbar^2}{2m\sigma^2}(x^2/\sigma^2 - 1)\psi}}. \tag{3.12}$$

For this equation to hold at all x, the terms in ψ must cancel, and separately those in $x^2\psi$ must also. In Eq. (3.12), the ends of the over and underbraces pick out corresponding terms. Getting groups of terms to cancel like this is a common technique in solving equations after having picked a solution. Hence

terms in ψ :
$$E_0 = \frac{\hbar^2}{2m\sigma^2} \tag{3.13}$$

terms in $x^2\psi$:
$$\frac{1}{2}m\omega^2 = \frac{\hbar^2}{2m\sigma^4}. \tag{3.14}$$

---

[2]Note we are now numbering the states from 0 (ground state), with 1 being the first excited state, and so on. We have thus departed from the other convention of $\psi_1, \psi_2, \ldots$

The latter equation gives the characteristic spread σ associated with ψ which when returned to the former equation gives the characteristic energy, thus

$$\sigma^2 = \frac{\hbar}{m\omega} = \frac{\hbar}{\sqrt{mq}} \tag{3.15}$$

$$E_0 = \tfrac{1}{2}\hbar\omega. \tag{3.16}$$

Recall the role the term σ^2 plays in Gaussians like $e^{-x^2/2\sigma^2}$; see Ex. 1.14 and remarks following that about the standard form of Gaussians.

So the energy of the ground state is not zero, as it would be for a classical particle that would just sink to the bottom of the $\tfrac{1}{2}qx^2$ well. It is higher both because of the quantum localisation energy ($\hbar$ is involved in E_0) and because this resistance to localisation forces the particle to explore V away from $x = 0$ (thus the well stiffness q also appears in E_0). The ground state energy $\tfrac{1}{2}\hbar\omega$ is the famous *zero-point energy* possessed by all quantum oscillators, even those of the generalised form we discuss later. The extent of the zero-point motion is $\sim \sigma$. Note that its extent depends on $\hbar$ and inversely on m — more massive particles have smaller quantum effects. See the examples of Ex. 2.5. Figure 3.5 shows the wavefunction in the potential. Importantly, the Gaussian wavefunction possesses minimal uncertainty, as

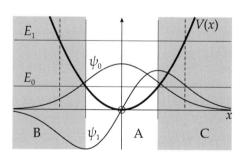

Figure 3.5: A harmonic potential $V(x)$ with $\psi_0(x)$ and $\psi_1(x)$. The particle penetrates the classically forbidden regions, B and C, of the ground state. Dotted lines mark the first excited state's forbidden regions. States have either even or odd symmetry.

explored under expectation values in Sect. 4.3 where we also deal with momentum.

Exercise 3.8: Deduce without calculation that the mean square position in the ground state, $\langle x^2 \rangle_0$, is $\sigma^2/2$.

We guess the first excited state wavefunction to be

$$\psi_1(x) = A_1 \frac{2x}{\sigma} e^{-x^2/2\sigma^2}. \tag{3.17}$$

It can be shown that for a confining potential symmetric about $x = 0$, the wavefunctions will have a definite symmetry, either even or odd; see Ex. 3.4. Our choice for ψ_1 is odd, thanks to the x pre-factor of the $e^{-x^2/2\sigma^2}$ in the choice of ψ_1 in Eq. (3.17). Theorems show that members of a family of eigenfunctions are, except for special cases, orthogonal to each other (in the sense of $\int_{-\infty}^{\infty} \psi_i\psi_j dx = 0$ for the ith and j^{th} functions ψ). The oddness of ψ_1 certainly ensures its orthogonality against ψ_0 (check why). The single node is also required by Sturm–Liouville theory if this is to be the next state in increasing energy.

Exercise 3.9: Show that the guessed ψ_1 in fact satisfies (3.11) but with an eigenvalue $E_1 = \frac{3}{2}\hbar\omega$. Show that σ^2 is as before; thus the wider spread of the first excited state's wavefunction into the potential is from the prefactor.

The prefactors to $e^{-x^2/2\sigma^2}$ in the ψ_i are the Hermite polynomials. They ensure both that the ψ_i are solutions to (3.11) and that they are orthogonal to each other, while providing the extra curvature and hence nodes for increasing eigen energy as required by Sturm–Liouville:

$$H_0(u) = 1, \quad H_1(u) = 2u, \quad H_2(u) = 4u^2 - 2, \quad \ldots. \qquad (3.18)$$

We then write $\psi_i(u) \propto H_i(u)e^{-u^2/2}$ where $u = x/\sigma$ is length reduced by the characteristic length σ. The eigen property of such ψ_i, expressed with the $H_i(x)$ factors, is in effect the definition of the Hermite polynomials. See Ex. 3.17, which also explores reduced variables further; Eq. (3.21), which defines these polynomials; and the explicit exercises of Ex. 1.35.

Orthogonality, being perpendicular in the case of vectors, and for functions having $\int \psi_k\psi_j du = 0$, is another key property of the eigenfunctions of the differential operators of Sturm–Liouville theory; see also remarks around Ex. 2.3, page 34, concerning the Legendre polynomials.

Incidentally, another property of such functions is completeness: that is, arbitrary functions on the same interval can be expressed as a weighted sum of all the ψ_i functions of the operator. This is akin to expressing a general vector in terms of a basis. See Eq. (1.50) in Sect. 1.2 for more details.

Exercise 3.10: Show that the first few $\psi_n = H_n(u)e^{-u^2/2}$ are indeed orthogonal. Why is it trivially so for $\int_{-\infty}^{\infty} \psi_0\psi_1 du$ and $\int_{-\infty}^{\infty} \psi_1\psi_2 du$? Explicitly show it for $\int_{-\infty}^{\infty} \psi_0\psi_2 du$.

Exercise 3.11: Show that $H_2(x/\sigma)$ in fact gives a ψ_2 that satisfies (3.11) but with an eigenvalue $E_2 = \frac{5}{2}\hbar\omega$.

Figure 3.5 confirms still more about the wavefunctions. Since the all-important curvature, that is the second derivative, is $d^2\psi/dx^2 = \frac{2m}{\hbar^2}(V - E)\psi$, then the second derivative of ψ_i vanishes at an x where $V(x) = E_i$; the corresponding wavefunction has a point of inflection there.

The eigenstates of the quantum SHO have a ladder of eigen energies

$$E_n = (n + \tfrac{1}{2})\hbar\omega. \tag{3.19}$$

One says that the system possesses n quanta (each of energy $\hbar\omega$) when in the nth state. The system can be quite general — for instance, in their quantised form, the harmonic oscillations of the electromagnetic field in the vacuum (black body radiation) or the collective oscillations of a crystal, are respectively *photons* and *phonons*. Such generalised harmonic oscillators are ubiquitous in nature. They are formally just like our oscillating parti-cle and underpin all of physics. In particular, these generalised oscillators are the fundamental objects in quantum electrodynamics, as mentioned on pages 33 and 43. In Chapter 5.3, after arming ourselves with a little more mathematics (partial derivatives), we quantise an oscillating string. It could equally be an electromagnetic or sound wave. We thus move away from zero dimensional objects (point particles) to 1-D objects (strings). We dis-cuss in Sect. 2.4 the observation of quantised levels via the discrete energies of emitted or absorbed photons. For the infinite square well the levels in-crease in energy as $\sim n^2$ where n is the state index or *principal quantum number*. For an atom, the quantum levels become more closely spaced as n grows larger. For the harmonic oscillator, the states are equally spaced.

3.3 Summary

The infinite square well presented a very idealised potential. Relaxing the infinite potential gives a more realistic problem. We derived the bound state wavefunctions and eigen energies corresponding to the finite square well. Furthermore, it is possible to find the particle outside the well, where classically it is forbidden since it would have negative kinetic energy. In addition to ensuring that a wavefunction is normalisable[3], we noted that wavefunctions and their first derivatives are continuous at boundaries.

---

[3]A necessary requirement is that $\psi(x) \to 0$ as $x \to \pm\infty$.

The second half of the chapter solved the quantum harmonic oscillator. This is the most important potential in the whole of physics and readers will be solving it in its various guises throughout their studies. We found the ground state to be a Gaussian, which possesses the minimum uncertainty permitted by Heisenberg's uncertainty principle. The excited states have extra nodes generated by the Hermite polynomials, which multiply the underlying Gaussian to give the full wavefunction. The energies form a uniform ladder of levels, equally spaced by $\hbar\omega$, starting at $\frac{1}{2}\hbar\omega$, which is the zero point energy. So $E_n = \hbar\omega\left(n + \frac{1}{2}\right)$ where $n \in \{0, 1, 2, \dots\}$.

3.4 Additional problems

Exercise 3.12: A particle is confined to a semi-infinite 1-D potential such that $V = \infty$ for $x \leq 0$, with $V = 0$ for $0 < x < a$ and $V = V_0$ for $x \geq a$. What condition is obeyed by the eigen energies? Analyse how many states the well has, and sketch some wavefunctions. At what V_0, for a given a, is the last state lost? Why is there a connection between this problem and the apparently rather different Ex. 3.3?

Exercise 3.13: A particle is confined to the 1-D potential shown in Fig. 3.6. The energy E_4 of the 4th bound state in the potential is shown. Sketch the corresponding wavefunction.

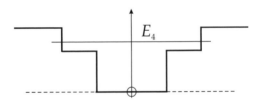

Figure 3.6: A stepped well potential with the 4th eigen energy indicated; see Ex. 3.13.

Exercise 3.14: *A particle is confined to a 1-D potential such that $V = \infty$ for $x \leq 0$ and $x \geq 2a$; and $V = 0$ for $0 < x < a$ and $V = V_0$ for $a \leq x < 2a$. Find an expression for the eigen energy, taking care to distinguish between states of different character (those with and those without exponential components). Sketch a few states. [Hint: in $a < x < 2a$ one needs solutions of both characters, i.e. both $e^{-k'x}$ and $e^{+k'x}$ when $E < V_0$ and both sine and cosine when $E > V_0$, in order to achieve $\psi(x = 2a) = 0$.]

Exercise 3.15: For the potential shown in Fig. 3.7, sketch the general form of the wavefunctions for the ground state (denoted by its energy E_0), for first excited state (E_1), and for a highly excited state (E_n). What is the parity (even or oddness) of the ground state?

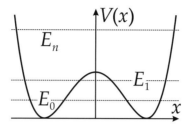

Figure 3.7: A double well potential with 3 eigen energies indicated; see Ex. 3.15.

Exercise 3.16: What are the quantised energies for a particle moving in a 1-D potential with $V = \infty$ for $x < 0$ and $V = \frac{1}{2}mw^2x^2$ for $x \geq 0$? Sketch a few states and comment on the connection with the quantum oscillator. Classically this is the impact oscillator which, when driven, is chaotic.

Exercise 3.17: Reduce lengths by the characteristic length, σ, of Eq. (3.15) so that $u = x/\sigma$ and reduce energy by $\frac{1}{2}\hbar w$ so that $\mathcal{E} = E/(\frac{1}{2}\hbar w)$. Show that the Schrödinger equation for SHM, Eq. (3.11), becomes

$$-\frac{d^2\psi}{du^2} + u^2\psi = \mathcal{E}\psi. \tag{3.20}$$

Show that if $\psi(u) = H(u)e^{-u^2/2}$, the Hermite polynomials are defined by

$$-\frac{d^2H}{du^2} + 2u\frac{dH}{du} + H = \mathcal{E}H. \tag{3.21}$$

Exercise 3.18: Find the positions of maximum probability when in the state ψ_2 of the simple harmonic oscillator. Do these positions correspond to the amplitude of the classical motion for a particle with this energy in this harmonic potential?

Exercise 3.19: It can be shown that in the 3-D problem of the H-atom the ground state wavefunction is spherically-symmetric (depends only on the radial distance r from the proton) and is $\psi_0(r) = A_0e^{-r/a_B}$ where A_0 is the normalisation ensuring $\int_0^\infty 4\pi r^2\psi_0^2\,dr = 1$. As before, a_B is the Bohr radius, Eq. (2.12). Note that ψ_0^2 is a probability density and the volume of an elementary spherical shell of radius r and thickness dr is $4\pi r^2 dr$ (area $\times$ thickness of shell). Thus $4\pi r^2 \psi_0^2$ is the radial probability density, that is probability per unit length radially. Find $\langle r \rangle$, $\langle r^2 \rangle$, and r_m, the radius with the maximal probability. Although A_0 is not required for these quantities (see Ex. 1.14), evaluate it for integration practice. Comment on the meaning of a_B hereby made more precise than in the argument leading to Eq. (2.12).

Exercise 3.20: Wavefunction matching
Show that ψ and $d\psi/dx$ are continuous except at pathological points.
Solution: Take for concreteness the Schrödinger equation in the form $\frac{d}{dx}\frac{d\psi}{dx} = -k^2\psi$. If its form suddenly changes to $\frac{d}{dx}\frac{d\psi}{dx} = k'^2\psi$ at the point x in question, the argument will not be affected[4]. Integrate the equation over a small interval $(x - \delta/2, x + \delta/2)$ spanning the point x where the form of ψ changes

$$\int_{x-\delta/2}^{x+\delta/2} \frac{d}{dz}\frac{d\psi}{dz}dz = -\int_{x-\delta/2}^{x+\delta/2} k^2\psi(x)dz.$$

Integrating,

$$\frac{d\psi}{dz}\bigg|_{x-\delta/2}^{x+\delta/2} = \frac{d\psi(x+\delta/2)}{dx} - \frac{d\psi(x-\delta/2)}{dx} = -\delta.k^2\psi.$$

We have reverted to the dummy variable z. We recognised that integration is the reverse of differentiation to undo one of the differentiations on the left hand side, and also used the fact on the right hand side that an integral over a small region is the length of the region times the value of the integrand in that region (see Fig. 1.7 and Ex. 1.11 for how to do this). As $\delta \to 0$ we have 0 on the right hand side and hence on the left hand side $\frac{d\psi}{dx}\big|_{x+\delta/2} = \frac{d\psi}{dx}\big|_{x-\delta/2}$, that is, the gradient is continuous. The only pathology that can occur is when on the right hand side $V \to \infty$ (and hence $k^2 \to \infty$) at a point x where we are letting $\delta \to 0$. Then right hand side becomes finite rather than vanishing; there is then a jump in the gradient $\frac{d\psi}{dx}\big|_{x+\delta/2} \neq \frac{d\psi}{dx}\big|_{x-\delta/2}$. Our infinite well was an example: $d\psi/dx$ was not continuous at $x = 0$ and $x = a$ where V misbehaved. The argument above, applied again on $d\psi/dx$ this time, shows that ψ is continuous, even at the pathological points of V.

---

[4]Indeed a $k^2(x)$, that is a potential $V(x)$, varying as the boundary is approached does not invalidate the argument that follows.

4

Foundations of quantum mechanics

de Broglie's Ansatz, the basis of Schrödinger's equation, operators, complex numbers and functions, momentum, free particle wavefunctions, expectation values

We return to the starting points of quantum mechanics and how to motivate Schrödinger's equation. The advances in the quantum mechanics of radiation by Planck and Einstein guided pioneers applying quantum mechanics to matter. We follow that route below and find that the operators which emerge require complex numbers. We thus first review imaginary numbers. We shall see that quantum mechanics is an intrinsically complex subject; ψ has in general both real and imaginary parts. We wander off into the complex plane and appreciate that momentum, free particles and their currents, and dynamics (Chapter 5) all require a complex ψ. Important problems such as barrier penetration and tunnelling become accessible to us.

4.1 Mathematical preliminaries — Complex numbers

What number, when squared, gives -1? We define the number i (alluding to *i*maginary) to have this property:

$$i^2 = -1 \quad \text{or equivalently} \quad \sqrt{-1} = i. \tag{4.1}$$

Imaginary numbers are not confined to have size 1, but can take a continuum of values iI where I is a real number in the interval $-\infty$ to $+\infty$.

The imaginary axis is conventionally drawn vertically, the real horizontally. When we combine real and imaginary numbers, $z = R + iI$, we get complex numbers, z, which sit in the complex plane and are sometimes written $z = x + iy$ for obvious reasons[1]; see the picture Fig. 4.1 of this plane, known as an Argand diagram. One might reasonably ask — are there still further

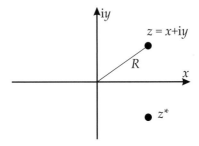

Figure 4.1: The complex plane of points $z = x + iy$, with absolute value or modulus R, and with complex conjugate z^*.

types of numbers? There are, for instance quaternions, octonions, Grassmanns, ..., but one can prove that extending reals to imaginary numbers is sufficient for our purposes here. A function can take complex values too, so for instance $\psi(x) = \psi_R(x) + i\psi_I(x)$ is broken down into its real and imaginary parts ψ_R and ψ_I (both real functions of x, but ψ_I is accompanied by i when in ψ). As we shall soon see, functions can also take complex arguments.

The usual rules of algebra apply:

$$z^2 = (x + iy)(x + iy) = x^2 - y^2 + 2ixy \tag{4.2}$$
$$zz' = (x + iy)(x' + iy') = xx' - yy' + i(x'y + xy'). \tag{4.3}$$

The $-$ in front of y^2 and yy' is from $i^2 = -1$. One gets a good feeling for complex numbers by placing them in the complex plane:

Exercise 4.1: Put the following numbers onto a complex plane diagram: i, $-1, -i, 1 + i, \frac{1}{i}, \frac{1+i}{\sqrt{2}}, \left(\frac{1+i}{\sqrt{2}}\right)^2, \left(\frac{-1+i}{\sqrt{2}}\right)^2.$

Hint: Some of these will require some evaluation before plotting. In particular get the imaginary numbers into the numerator by multiplying fraction

---

[1] It is sometimes conventional in engineering to use j rather than i.

top and bottom by the same suitable number. What does plotting the final two tell you about $\sqrt{}$ on the complex plane?

The size or magnitude of a complex number is its distance from the origin (much like the length of a radius vector, but in the complex plane). For $x + iy$, the radius vector is $\sqrt{x^2 + y^2}$ (Pythagoras). It is called the modulus of (sometimes called the absolute value of) z, written $|z|$. Confirm that the square of this distance is $|z|^2 = x^2 + y^2$ which can be written $(x + iy)(x - iy)$. When every i in z is replaced by $-i$, the result is called $z^* = x - iy$, and is known as the *complex conjugate* of z. Thus the modulus squared is $|z|^2 = zz^*$ and, from the above, is guaranteed to be real. For instance:

$$\psi\psi^* = |\psi|^2 = (\psi_R + i\psi_I)(\psi_R - i\psi_I) = \psi_R^2 + \psi_I^2. \tag{4.4}$$

Note that $(z^*)^* = z$.

Exercise 4.2: What are the moduli of the numbers in Ex. 4.1? You may need to reconsider your drawing in that exercise!

Solution: $1, 1, 1, \sqrt{2}, 1, 1, 1, 1$.

Two useful properties of z are

$$z + z^* = 2x \qquad\qquad z - z^* = 2iy \tag{4.5}$$

$$x = \frac{1}{2}(z + z^*) \qquad\qquad y = \frac{1}{2i}(z - z^*), \tag{4.6}$$

which are good routes to the real and imaginary parts that are needed below.

Exercise 4.3: If z is a complex number, what is the modulus and phase of $Z = \frac{z}{z^*}$ in terms of those of z?

Complex exponentials

Let us revisit the differential equation of the SHM type

$$\frac{d^2\psi}{dx^2} = -k^2\psi, \tag{4.7}$$

with the general solution $\psi = A\sin(kx) + B\cos(kx)$. We have repeatedly noticed the tantalising similarity between this equation and the exponential type of equation with $k^2 \rightarrow -k^2$, that is to $\frac{d^2\psi}{dx^2} = k^2\psi$ with $\psi = Ce^{kx} + De^{-kx}$ in general. We could try complex exponentials $e^{\pm ikx}$ in Eq. (4.7). Twice differentiating the exponential gives $(\pm ik)^2 e^{\pm ikx} = -k^2 e^{\pm ikx}$, and thus $e^{\pm ikx}$ are also solutions to the SHM equation. But since (4.7) is a second order differential equation, there are at most two independent solutions and hence the $e^{\pm ikx}$ must be combinations of $\sin(kx)$ and $\cos(kx)$.

Exercise 4.4: Prove that $\cos u = \frac{1}{2}\left(e^{iu} + e^{-iu}\right)$ and $\sin u = \frac{1}{2i}\left(e^{iu} - e^{-iu}\right)$.

Solution: In the first potential well problems, we fixed the constants weighting the two components to ψ by fitting to a boundary condition. Here we fix the weights of e^{iu} and e^{-iu} in $\cos u$ by checking that their combination is such that it reproduces $\cos 0 = 1$. This is trivially true since $e^0 = 1$ and thus at $u = 0$ we have $\frac{1}{2}(1 + 1) = 1$. The combination in $\sin u$ must also be correct since differentiating $\sin$ gives $\cos$ and differentiating $\left(e^{iu} - e^{-iu}\right)$ gives $i\left(e^{iu} + e^{-iu}\right)$ which on dividing by 2i yields the expression for cos.

Exercise 4.5: Show $e^{iu} = \cos u + i\sin u$ and $e^{-iu} = \cos u - i\sin u$.

Exercise 4.6: Draw on the complex plane the position of $z = Re^{i\theta}$ for $\theta = 0$, $\pi/4$, $\pi/2$, $3\pi/4$, π, 2π. Clearly R is the modulus (prove $|z|^2 = R^2$) while θ is known as the argument (or phase) of z, sometimes written $\arg(z)$. For a given θ draw in z^* (reflection is involved). What is the argument of z^*?

It is made explicit by Ex. 4.6 and by the expression $e^{iu} = \cos u + i\sin u$ that e^{iu} is function periodic in u, with period 2π, quite unlike e^u.

Exercise 4.7: Draw the trajectory of $z(t) = e^{i\omega t}$ on the complex plane. What is the motion of $x(t)$ and $y(t)$ on the real and imaginary axes? How long is one period, T.

Solution: The complex number $z = \cos(\omega t) + i\sin(\omega t)$ has unit modulus, so as t evolves, z moves around the unit circle uniformly. Since $e^{2\pi i} = 1$ (the argument 2π takes us back to where we started), then the period must be such that $\omega T = 2\pi$, that is, $T = 2\pi/\omega$.

The real and imaginary parts of $e^{i\omega t}$ are out of phase with each other, for instance when $\cos(\omega t) = 1$, then $\sin(\omega t) = 0$ and *vice versa*. In fact the two parts, which are the projections of the circular motion onto the x and

y axes, are like simple harmonic oscillations. The argument of z, that is ωt here, gives the phase of the motion.

Evaluating the phase (argument) of complex numbers

We have seen that the modulus $|z|$ of the complex number $z = Re^{i\theta}$ is R. Writing $z = R(\cos\theta + i\sin\theta)$ we have $\text{Re}(z) = R\cos(\theta)$ and $\text{Im}(z) = R\sin(\theta)$ where $\text{Re}(z)$ is the real part of z and $\text{Im}(z)$ is the imaginary part. Taking their ratio eliminates R and gives $\tan\theta = \text{Im}(z)/\text{Re}(z)$, a result we shall later find useful (and which is useful in any part of physics where phases arise). Note that if the imaginary part of z is zero, $\text{Im}(z) = 0$, that is we have a real number, then the argument is zero. An equivalent expression for the argument is:

$$\arg(z) = \tan^{-1}\left(\frac{\text{Im}(z)}{\text{Re}(z)}\right). \tag{4.8}$$

Use for instance Eqs. (4.5–4.6) to get the real and imaginary parts to put in the expression (4.8). See Fig. 4.1 for $\theta = \arg(z)$. Clearly, $\arg(z^*) = -\theta$.

Hyperbolic functions

We have seen that $\sin x$ and $\cos x$ can be expressed in terms of complex exponentials. Indeed, they can be seen as the definitions of the trigonometric functions. Because the combination of the sum and difference of real exponentials also appears very often, they are given a special name — hyperbolic functions. So, we define the functions

$$\sinh x = \frac{1}{2}\left(e^x - e^{-x}\right) \tag{4.9}$$

$$\cosh x = \frac{1}{2}\left(e^x + e^{-x}\right) \tag{4.10}$$

$$\tanh x = \frac{\sinh x}{\cosh x} = \frac{e^x - e^{-x}}{e^x + e^{-x}}. \tag{4.11}$$

The complex exponentials for the trigonometrical functions[2] are replaced by real exponentials. These functions are plotted in Fig. 4.2. Accordingly, many trigonometrical identities carry over but with possible sign changes.

---

[2]Trigonometrical functions are also referred to as *circular* functions because they describe parametrically a circle. Similiarly, hyperbolic functions describe hyperbolae.

Figure 4.2:   The   hyperbolic   functions   (a) $\sinh(x)$, (b) $\cosh(x)$ and (c) $\tanh(x)$. Note which are   even   and   which are odd functions, and that the asymptotes of $\tanh(x)$ are ± 1.

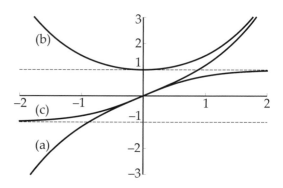

Exercise 4.8: Show that the hyperbolic functions are related to the trigono-metrical ones by

$$\sinh x = -i\sin(ix),$$
$$\cosh x = \cos(ix),$$
$$\tanh x = -i\tan(ix),$$

and the equivalent of the Pythagorean identity is

$$\cosh^2 x - \sinh^2 x = 1.$$

Exercise 4.9: Find the derivatives of $\sinh x$, $\cosh x$ and $\tanh x$. What is the asymptotic (large argument, positive and negative) behaviour of $\sinh(x)$ and $\cosh(x)$?

4.2 Foundations of Quantum Mechanics

We have gradually introduced the ideas of quantum mechanics, attempting to give the reader a feel for the subject by solving problems. One might feel dissatisfied by how apparently *ad hoc* this approach is. We adopted the machinery of (i) a wavefunction describing a quantum mechanical system in its entirety, and (ii) of operators acting on wavefunctions to return values for their corresponding physical variables. The Schrödinger operator equation $(\hat{T} + \hat{V})\psi = E\psi$ for the wavefunction corresponds to the classical mechanics relation $T + V = E$. We assumed a form for $\hat{T}$ and postulated that ψ would describe the quantum mechanical system in its entirety. We quote from Messiah's monumental book[3] on quantum mechanics:

> No deductive reasoning can lead us to that equation (Schrödinger's). Like all equations of mathematical physics, it must be postulated and its only justification lies in the success of the comparison of its predictions with experimental results.

In some sense we are doing as well as can be done. Later courses on quantum mechanics can more easily take a formal axiomatic approach when one already has some feel for this deeply counterintuitive subject, and has more of the required mathematical machinery and fluency.

Two slit experiment

The classic experiment of quantum physics is that of the double slit or Young's slit experiment. Originally performed by Thomas Young in 1803 to support the wave theory of light and overthrow the prevailing corpuscular (particle) theory of Newton, the double slit experiment can be performed with electrons, light (photons), atoms and molecules with identical results.

Let us consider a collimated beam of electrons illuminating two slits in an opaque plate; see Fig. 4.3. The observation screen on the far side records the arrival of a particle — for instance, it could be a photographic plate that reacts chemically when an electron's energy is deposited at a localised point. We find a wave-like interference pattern on the screen. The interpretation is that electron waves diffract through the double slits before interfering with each other and giving a sinusoidal pattern of the total $\psi(x)$ on the plate and hence a squared sinusoidal pattern for $P(x)$. Figure 4.3(b) shows waves setting off from the two slits. When the phase difference $k\Delta l = kd\sin\theta = 2n\pi$ for integer n, there is constructive interference and a maximum of ψ and hence also $P(x)$. See Ex. 1.22 for how to explicitly add two such waves.

However, the effect persists even when we have a single electron passing through the apparatus. Figure 4.3(a) shows a pattern of individual arrivals of particles building up to the expected $P(x)$. See the Hitachi research webpage[4] for an experiment which instead uses a beam of atoms diffracting through two slits. The associated movie of the build up of particle numbers in time on the detector is particularly fascinating. A given particle evidently (considered in its wave-like form) goes through *both* slits and the two parts

---

[3]Quantum Mechanics, Vols I & II, A. Messiah, North Holland (1961)
[4]http://www.hitachi.com/rd/research/em/doubleslit.html

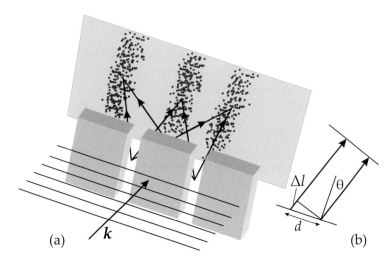

Figure 4.3: (a) A particle plane wave (a beam of particles) is incident on a barrier with two slits. Crests of constant phase are shown normal to the wavevector **k**. Cylindrical waves are diffracted from each of the slits towards a detector plate. Wavevectors perpendicular to the circular sections of constant phase from each slit are shown in the cases where there is constructive interference — the path differences give a phase difference which is a multiple of 2π. (b) Wavevectors emanating from the slits separated by a distance d and propagating at an angle θ have a path difference $\Delta l = d \sin \theta$ for a distant plate.

of its wavefunction interfere! At the screen, the wavefunction collapses as the spatial position is recorded. Interference from particles is one of the least intuitive results in the whole of physics if one remains rigidly bound to a particle-like picture[5].

We cannot predict with certainty where any given electron will fall but a large number will give the probability distribution ("$\cos^2$ fringes"). This suggests that the probability of an electron being detected at a particular point is given by the amplitude squared of a wave(function). The intensity of a wave is the amplitude squared in classical physics.

Finally, if we close off one of the slits completely, the interference pattern disappears and we recover particle-like behaviour due to the collapse of the

---

[5]"Anyone who is not shocked by quantum theory has not understood it." — Niels Bohr, a founder of quantum mechanics.

wavefunction after measurement (our knowing which slit is traversed).

Deducing the momentum operator

Apart from correspondence to classical mechanics, the Schrödinger equation should be linear so that we can superpose its wave-like solutions and describe observed interference phenomena. Additionally, de Broglie boldly hypothesised that matter waves (the quantum mechanical description of particles) should have important commonality with the known quantum properties of light, that is with electromagnetic waves. For light of wavelength λ and frequency ν, the energy and momentum are given by

$$\lambda = h/p \qquad\qquad \nu = E/h \qquad\qquad (4.12)$$

or
$$p = \hbar k \qquad\qquad E = \hbar\omega, \qquad\qquad (4.13)$$

where $k = 2\pi/\lambda$ is the wavevector and $\omega = 2\pi\nu$ is the angular frequency. For matter, the operator for momentum is taken to be

$$\hat{p} = -i\hbar\frac{d}{dx} \qquad\qquad (4.14)$$

and replaces its appearance classically. Recall that in quantum mechanics it is momentum that is fundamental, rather than velocity. We delay time-dependence and hence E operators until Chapter 5. So we can see that since $T = p^2/2m$, then $\hat{T} = \hat{p}^2/2m$ gives $\hat{T} = -\frac{\hbar^2}{2m}\frac{d^2}{dx^2}$ as we originally assumed. One could have instead started with (4.14) and derived the Schrödinger equation.

Let us check the consistency of this definition. Free particles (simple waves) or particles in a spatially constant potential $V_0 < E$ have the eigen equation $\hat{T}\psi = (E - V_0)\psi$. For $\psi \propto e^{\pm ikx}$ or for $\sin(kx)$ and $\cos(kx)$ one has

$$(E - V_0)\psi = -\frac{\hbar^2}{2m}\frac{d^2\psi}{dx^2} = \frac{\hbar^2 k^2}{2m}\psi, \quad \text{that is} \quad T = (E - V_0) = \frac{\hbar^2 k^2}{2m}$$

on cancelling out ψ. For $p = \hbar k$ (de Broglie's hypothesis), one has $T = p^2/2m$, which is a correspondence to classical physics. Additionally, $-i\hbar\frac{d}{dx}$ applied to free particle solutions like e^{ikx} does give $\hat{p}\psi = -i\hbar\frac{d\psi}{dx} = \hbar k\psi = p\psi$. We see that the choice in (4.14) for $\hat{p}$ is indeed consistent with p in (4.13).

Changing the energy of a free particle changes its momentum and hence its wavelength. It is useful to know figures for the wavelength of particles. Electrons can be diffracted around objects of size comparable to their wavelength. They can be used, in an electron microscope, to examine objects much as visible light is used in an optical microscope. But then their wavelength must be much shorter than the size of the object being examined so diffractive effects are minimal. Using the above relations, one has for the so-called de Broglie wavelength

$$\lambda = h/\sqrt{2mE}. \tag{4.15}$$

For an electron of energy $E = 1$ eV, the wavelength is 1.2×10^{-9} m, which is about a nanometre; see also Ex. 2.5. More energetic electrons than these are required to see the atomic structure of solids. Further decreases in λ follow as $1/\sqrt{E}$.

Is there an eigen equation for momentum instead? It would have to be $\hat{p}\psi = p\psi$, where $\hat{p}$ is an operator and p is its eigenvalue, the value of the momentum of the state represented by ψ if it is an eigenfunction. Trying out the above eigenfunctions of the energy operator for a free particle (free particles being the only candidates for a well-defined momentum), one finds

$$\hat{p}e^{ikx} = \hbar k e^{ikx} \qquad\qquad \hat{p}\sin(kx) = -i\hbar k \cos(kx)$$
$$\hat{p}e^{-ikx} = -\hbar k e^{-ikx} \qquad\qquad \hat{p}\cos(kx) = i\hbar k \sin(kx).$$

The functions $e^{\pm ikx}$ are eigenfunctions (one ends up on the right hand side with a multiple of the function that was acted upon on the left hand side), and the eigenvalues are $p = \hbar k$, $p = -\hbar k$. Momentum is along $+x$ for e^{ikx} and along $-x$ for e^{-ikx}. Essentially k is a vector — in 1-D we only sense direction by the accompanying sign. However sin and cos are not eigenfunctions. Since they are combinations of e^{ikx} and e^{-ikx}, they contain $p = \hbar k$ and $p = -\hbar k$ in equal measure and are thus not pure momentum states. In fact our well solutions show they are standing waves.

Other formulations of quantum mechanics

We note that there are other formulations of quantum mechanics. Heisenberg's matrix mechanics is equivalent to, but seemingly very different from Schrödinger's approach. Operators can be matrices acting on vectors, called state vectors, that describe the system. The eigenstates are eigenvectors that when acted upon by the operator return the same vector multiplied by an eigenvalue. These eigenvalues correspond to possible values observed for the physical variable represented by this operator; see also the discussion of matrices after Ex. 2.3. A third formulation of quantum mechanics was invented by Feynman during his doctoral work based on the principle of least action. This sum over histories or path integral approach involves

adding up the probability amplitudes of all possible paths that a particle
might take between the start and end points. Each amplitude is given by
e^{iS}, where the integral of the difference between kinetic and potential energies $S = \int [T - V(x)] \, dx$ is the *action* of the particular path $x(t)$. Feynman's
formulation is particularly powerful in the development of quantum field
theory.

4.3   Expectation values of states

The expectation value is what one obtains as the result of many measurements. For instance $\psi(x)$ leads to the probability of finding the particle at
x. An individual measurement of position collapses the wavefunction and
a definite result, one of the eigenvalues of the operator, is achieved. This
is postulate 4 of our list. Many measurements of position builds up $P(x)$
as a distribution of outcomes. A realisation of this is the buildup of the
interference pattern of electron waves from the two slit experiment.

As discussed in Sect. 1.2, the expected value of a classical quantity (which
maybe a function of, say, position x) is

$$\langle f(x) \rangle = \int f(x) P(x) \, dx.$$

The quantum generalisation is

$$\langle \hat{O}(x) \rangle = \int \psi^*(x) \hat{O}(x) \psi(x) \, dx. \tag{4.16}$$

Notice that the observable of interest is an operator that acts on the wavefunction describing the physical state. The appearance of the complex conjugate ensures consistency with the requirement that the wavefunction gen-
erates a probability distribution $|\psi(x)|^2 = P(x)$. Let us consider some ex-
amples to explain in greater detail.

Energy eigenstates

The expectation values of eigenstates of the Hamiltonian are of particular
interest as they represent solutions of the Schrödinger equation. The expectation of energy is an important example; take the energy eigen equation
(Schrödinger's) $E_n \psi_n = (\hat{T} + V)\psi_n$ with ψ_n an energy eigenfunction, mul-

tiply it from the left by ψ_n^* and integrate

$$\int \psi_n^*(x) E_n \psi_n(x)\, dx = \int \left[\psi_n^*(x)\hat{T}\psi_n(x) + \psi_n^*(x)V\psi_n(x) \right]\, dx \qquad (4.17)$$

$$E_n = \int \left[\psi_n^*(x)\hat{T}\psi_n(x) + \psi_n^*(x)V\psi_n(x) \right]\, dx. \qquad (4.18)$$

E_n is just a constant and comes out of the integral. Then one has $\int \psi_n^* \psi_n dx = \int |\psi_n|^2 dx = \int P(x) dx = 1$, where $P(x) = |\psi_n|^2$ is the probability density, and one has (4.18). The potential operator $V(x)$ should really have a hat, which was taken off as explained before and after Eq. (2.3), since the value of the function $V(x)$ is being returned. The order of factors in the last term can be re-written to show its meaning better: $\int \psi_n^*(x)\psi_n(x)V dx = \int P(x)V(x)dx = \langle V(x) \rangle$. The $\langle \ldots \rangle$ indicate average (over $P(x)$). The first term is written as $\langle \hat{T} \rangle$ and hence $E_n = \langle \hat{T} \rangle + \langle V(x) \rangle$. See Sect. 4.3 for expectation in superposition of eigenstates. One might think this is a method of getting E. Indeed very powerful (variational) estimation methods rest on this idea, by guessing ψ and then varying this guess; but in general one needs an eigen solution ψ and in generating this solution, one has probably already generated E_n. However, knowing expectation values of relevant physical variables is very important in quantum mechanics.

Exercise 4.10: Taking $\hat{O}(x) = \hat{x} = x$, calculate $\langle \hat{x} \rangle$ for the eigenfunctions of the infinite square well.

Exercise 4.11: Find $\langle \hat{p} \rangle$ for $\psi = Ae^{ikx}$, a plane wave.
Solution: $\langle \hat{p} \rangle = -i\hbar \int A^* e^{-ikx} \frac{d}{dx} Ae^{ikx} dx = \hbar k \int A^* A\, dx$. We have used $\left(e^{ikx} \right)^* = e^{-ikx}$, then differentiated e^{ikx}, and finally used $e^{-ikx}.e^{ikx} = e^0 = 1$. A technical difficulty for free, plane waves is that the coefficient A is hard to define — one can put the wave in a large box of length L and then $A \propto 1/\sqrt{L}$. But in any event, if A is a good normalisation, it means that $\int A^* A dx = 1$ and $\langle \hat{p} \rangle = \hbar k$ as expected from de Broglie, Eq. (4.13).

Exercise 4.12: Show that $\langle \hat{p} \rangle = 0$ for the eigenfunctions of the infinite square well.

The expectation values $\langle x^2 \rangle$ and $\langle p^2 \rangle$ for the quantum SHO are important.

Exercise 4.13: Evaluate $\langle x^2 \rangle$ and $\langle \hat{p}^2 \rangle$ for the ground state of the SHO.

Hint: The spatial probability is $P(x) \propto e^{-x^2/\sigma^2}$, a Gaussian, though not quite in the standard form explained around Ex. 1.14. Deduce $\langle x^2 \rangle$. Write down $\langle \hat{p}^2 \rangle$ in terms of the operator and the wavefunction, and reduce expressions to otherwise known quantities. See also Ex. 3.8.

The uncertainty in position and momentum are $\Delta x = \sqrt{\langle x^2 \rangle}$ and $\Delta p = \sqrt{\langle \hat{p}^2 \rangle}$ respectively. The results of Ex. 4.13 should give you

$$\Delta x . \Delta p = \tfrac{1}{2}\hbar \tag{4.19}$$

(confirm this). In other words the Heisenberg uncertainty inequality becomes an equality for the SHO ground state. Localisation by this kind of potential gives the minimal uncertainty in position while minimising the associated uncertainty in momentum[6].

Exercise 4.14: Show that $\Delta x . \Delta p = \tfrac{3}{2}\hbar$ for the SHO's first excited state with $\psi_1 = A_1.(2x/\sigma)e^{-x^2/2\sigma^2}$.

Superposition of eigenstates

We have thus far seen only where the system is in one of the eigenstates of the operator in question. In our case the operator was mostly the energy operator, though we have just met eigenstates of the momentum operator. A system in a superposed state if it is in an admixture of eigenstates. For instance, $\psi(x) = c_1\psi_1(x) + c_2\psi_2(x)$, is not an eigenstate of the energy operator $\hat{T} + V$, even if the component states ψ_1 and ψ_2 *are* eigenstates.

Exercise 4.15: Suppose that ψ_1 and ψ_2 are eigenstates of the Hamiltonian with different eigenvalues. Show that $\psi(x) = c_1\psi_1(x) + c_2\psi_2(x)$ is not an eigenstate of the energy operator if c_1 and c_2 are both non-zero.

Hint: Operate on ψ with the operator in question and inspect the result.

The weights c_1 and c_2 must be such that $\int P(x)\,dx = 1$. Probability is normalised.

---

[6]There is a fundamental reason for this property that a later course on quantum mechanics will cover. The transformation to the conjugate space, $x \rightarrow p$, happens to be one that transforms the Gaussian wavefunction in x into a Gaussian in p, that is the functional form is the same and this is what allows both uncertainties to be simultaneously optimised.

Exercise 4.16: Prove that, in a superposed state $\psi(x) = c_1\psi_1(x) + c_2\psi_2(x) + \ldots$, normalisation demands $|c_1|^2 + |c_2|^2 + \cdots = 1$.

Solution: Normalisation as a probability requires that $\int \psi^*(x)\psi(x)dx = 1$. If we put in $\psi(x) = c_1\psi_1(x) + c_2\psi_2(x) + \ldots$ we end up with terms to integrate that look like $c_i^* c_j \int \psi_i(x)^* \psi_j(x)dx$. Recall Sturm–Liouville theory dictates, by orthogonality of eigenstates, that this integral $= 0$ except when we have $i = j$. That is we only have corresponding terms surviving out of the sea of terms arising when we multiply the series for $\psi_i(x)^*$ and $\psi_i(x)$ together when taking $\int \psi_i(x)^* \psi_i(x)dx = 1$ (we have normalised wavefunctions). So we only get terms like $|c_i|^2$, and that leads us to the answer.

The above problem alludes to the completeness of Sturm–Liouville problems: any wavefunction can be expressed in terms of a linear combination of eigenfunctions. The coefficients c_i are the equivalent of the v_i coefficients of Eq. (1.50) in Sect. 1.2. In both cases, they measure the "overlap" of the wavefunction or vector with the eigenstates or co-ordinate basis, respectively. Thus the integral to evaluate the wavefunction coefficients,

$$c_i = \int \psi_i^*(x)\psi(x)\,dx, \qquad (4.20)$$

is a generalisation of the scalar product for conventional vectors $v_i = e_i \cdot v$. The vectors e_i are the coordinate vectors i, j and k for $i = 1, 2, 3$, respectively. Equation (4.20) extracts c_i and hence the weight $|c_i|^2$ of the ith state in ψ.

Exercise 4.17: Prove that the energy expectation value of a superposed state is $\langle \hat{H} \rangle = \sum_i |c_i|^2 E_i$.

Hint: Proceed analogously with the right hand sides of Eqs. (4.17) and (4.18) but using the full wavefunction ψ rather than just an eigenstate ψ_n.

These observations are very suggestive of the definition of expectation value for a discrete variable, $\langle E \rangle = \sum_i p_i E_i$, in this case energy. The interpretation of these $|c_i|^2$ weights is the probability upon measurement of obtaining the state i. That this is true is, in fact, a postulate of quantum mechanics. Here $\int \psi^* \hat{H} \psi \, dx$ yields a (probability) weighted combination of the outcomes E_n of the measurements of energy. We shall see that superposed states of the energy operator have very interesting time dependence.

4.4   Quantum particle currents

The flow j of particle probability in quantum mechanics is given by

$$j = \frac{i\hbar}{2m}\left(\psi\frac{d}{dx}\psi^* - \psi^*\frac{d}{dx}\psi\right) \equiv -\frac{\hbar}{m}\mathrm{Im}\left(\psi\frac{d\psi^*}{dx}\right). \tag{4.21}$$

It is conventionally called the *particle current* or *flux*. A proof is relatively simple, see Ex. 5.16, but we can see that we are along the right lines. The $-i\hbar\frac{d\psi}{dx}$ parts of the expression suggest we are dealing with expectations of momentum, and the $\frac{1}{m}$ converts it to a velocity-like object ($v = p/m$) upon which a current must rest. Further, thinking about $\psi\frac{d}{dx}\psi^*$ as the complex quantity χ, then the bracket in Eq. (4.21) is $\chi - \chi^* = 2i\,\mathrm{Im}(\chi)$, whereupon the 2s cancel and the $-i \times i = 1$ so that overall we have $j = \frac{\hbar}{m}\mathrm{Im}(\psi\frac{d}{dx}\psi^*)$. We see again that complexity is essential in quantum mechanics. Real wavefunctions, where $\psi^* = \psi$, would give $j = 0$ in Eq. (4.21). Only complex wavefunctions can give rise to particle flux. Our free particle states $\psi_\pm = A_\pm e^{\pm ikx}$ are complex. The bound states were described by real wavefunctions such as $\sin(kx)$, $\cos(kx)$ and $e^{\pm kx}$; no net current is carried in such standing waves.

Exercise 4.18: Explicitly evaluate j for Ae^{-ikx}, Be^{-kx} and $C\cos(kx)$.

Solution: Verify that one obtains $-\frac{\hbar k}{m}|A|^2$, 0, 0. Indeed we see in the first result momentum $p = \hbar k$ and thus a velocity-like object p/m. The current also depends on the magnitude $|A|^2$ of the probability, and is directed along $-x$.

Exercise 4.19: What is the current associated with the wavefunction $\psi = Ae^{ikx} + Be^{-ikx}$ [A and B possibly complex.] Interpret your result. It is of significance in barrier and step problems: Exs. 4.24–4.29.

Particle flux onto steps

We now see what happens when a current of quantum mechanical particles impinges on a potential step, Fig. 4.4. Two situations can arise: (A) the energy is less than the height of the step, $E < V_0$, or (B) it is greater, $E > V_0$. In the region of the step in case (A) we have negative kinetic energy and hence decaying exponential wavefunctions, and for (B) we have positive kinetic energy and complex oscillatory waves.

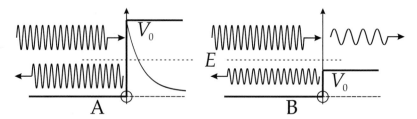

Figure 4.4: Free particle waves from $x < 0$ impinging on a potential step of height V_0 starting at $x = 0$. A: their energy E is less than the step height; they are reflected with exponential penetration into the step. B: their energy is greater; they are partially reflected and partially transmitted over the step.

Case A $(E < V_0)$ has wavefunctions:

For $x < 0$ $\psi_+ = A_+ e^{ikx}$ $\psi_- = A_- e^{-ikx}$

For $x > 0$ $\psi_A = A e^{-k'x}$

with $k = \sqrt{2mE}/\hbar$ and $k' = \sqrt{2m(V_0 - E)}/\hbar$ and where e^{+ikx} is a forward propagating wave, and e^{-ikx} propagates backwards. Recall for instance Ex. 4.18 which identifies the momentum in the latter wave, or think of $\pm\hbar k$ for the momenta.

Case B $(E > V_0)$ has:

For $x < 0$ $\psi_+ = B_+ e^{ikx}$ $\psi_- = B_- e^{-ikx}$

For $x > 0$ $\psi_B = B e^{ik''x}$

with $k = \sqrt{2mE}/\hbar$ and $k'' = \sqrt{2m(E - V_0)}/\hbar$. There is no counter propagating ($\leftarrow$) wave in B since in this semi-infinite step there is no possible source (or reflection) to the right of the step. In Fig. 4.4 we schematically show the oscillatory wavefunctions, though of course they are complex — one could take the picture to be the real parts perhaps, that is $A_\pm \cos(kx)$, and $B_\pm \cos(kx)$ with $B \cos(k''x)$. We show in case B oscillations to be of a longer wavelength above the step since $\lambda = 2\pi/k$ and $\lambda'' = 2\pi/k''$. Longer wavelength is expected at lower kinetic energy. Substituting k and k'' (with $h = 2\pi\hbar$) we find

$$\lambda = h/\sqrt{2mE} = h/p \quad \text{and} \quad \lambda'' = h/\sqrt{2m(E - V_0)} = h/p'' > \lambda.$$

This is as expected from de Broglie, and also from Sturm–Liouville: above the step, lower kinetic energy means less curvature, nodes further spaced, and thus longer wavelength.

The conditions of continuity of ψ and of $d\psi/dx$ (wavefunction matching) allow us to solve the problem entirely. Consult the solution of the finite square well for the method and for the conditions on ψ — see around Eqs. (3.5–3.7) on page 51. Considering cases A and B in parallel, we have for the continuity:

$$A_+ + A_- = A \qquad\qquad B_+ + B_- = B$$
$$ik(A_+ - A_-) = -k'A \qquad\qquad ik(B_+ - B_-) = ik''B$$

which can be solved for the weights of the various component wavefunctions:

Reflection	$A_- = A_+ \dfrac{k' + ik}{k' - ik}$	$B_- = B_+ \dfrac{k - k''}{k + k''}$
Transmission	$A = A_+ \dfrac{2k'}{k' - ik}$	$B = B_+ \dfrac{2k}{k + k''}.$

We have solved for A_-, A, B_- and B, that is the scales of the reflected and transmitted waves, in terms of the incident wave amplitudes A_+ or B_+. Although the A and B results look superficially similar, they in fact differ qualitatively.

Firstly, in case A, the reflected wave amplitude modulus squared is $|A_-|^2 = |A_+|^2 \left|\frac{k'+ik}{k'-ik}\right|^2$. The latter factor is $\frac{k'+ik}{k'-ik}\left(\frac{k'+ik}{k'-ik}\right)^*$ which becomes $\frac{k'+ik}{k'-ik}\frac{k'-ik}{k'+ik}$ on reversing the signs of i to get the complex conjugate (the *); overall the resultant number is clearly $= 1$. Therefore A_- and A_+ only differ in argument, but not modulus. Thus $A_- = A_+ e^{i\theta}$, where θ is the argument of $(k' + ik)/(k' - ik)$. The reflected wave is the same magnitude as the incident wave (total reflection), but is shifted from it in phase. Note that we have total *external* reflection (in contrast to total internal reflection as in optics).

Exercise 4.20: Show that the phase shift (argument) of the totally reflected wave with respect to the incident wave is given by $\tan\theta = 2kk'/(k'^2 + k^2) = 2\sqrt{E(V_0 - E)}/V_0$ on substituting for k and k'. Draw $\tan\theta$ as a function of $E/V_0 \le 1$, the incident energy normalised by the step energy. Note interesting behaviour around $E \sim 0$ and $E \sim V_0$, and show that the maximum phase shift is $\theta = \pi/4$.

Hint: Expressions such as $(k' + ik)/(k' - ik)$ need to have their complex factors taken into the numerator. Thus multiply top and bottom by the complex conjugate of the denominator. The real and imaginary parts are now easy to identify and share a common denominator which cancels on taking Im/Re; see Eq. (4.8).

The wavefunction that penetrates the classically forbidden region under the step differs in both modulus and phase from the incident wave since the pre-factor $2k'/(k' - ik)$ to the exponential is not of unit modulus and is not real. Since $\psi_A \sim e^{-k'x}$, it extends a characteristic distance $d' \sim 1/k' = \hbar/\sqrt{2m(V_0 - E)}$. Thus as the incident energy E approaches the barrier height V_0, the wave penetrates ever further into the step.

Exercise 4.21: Find the modulus and phase of $2k'/(k' - ik)$, and hence the connection between the evanescent (exponentially decaying) wave and the incident wave. Confirm that the wave in the forbidden region carries no current of particles into the potential step. The reflection is therefore total.

Secondly, in case B, the transmitted wave is now complex and can carry current. The reflected wave no longer differs in phase from the incident wave since $B_-/B_+ = (k - k'')/(k + k'')$ is purely real. This ratio is clearly less than 1 and the diminished reflected amplitude compared with the incident wave is depicted in Fig. 4.4B. The transmitted wave also has no phase shift since the ratio $B/B_+ = 2k/(k + k'')$ is real. The figure also emphasises the longer wavelength from the diminished, but still positive, kinetic energy.

By putting the various waves into the expression (4.21) for the current j, one can show that $j_+ = |B_+|^2 \frac{\hbar k}{m}$, $j_- = -|B_-|^2 \frac{\hbar k}{m}$ and $j_B = |B|^2 \frac{\hbar k''}{m}$. Note the sign in j_-; quantum mechanical current flows backwards (in negative x direction) in this wave (see Ex.4.19). Note each j carries a measure of its intensity (modulus squared) and the relevant wave vector factor (k or k''), appearing in the velocity-like combination $\hbar k/m$ that we discussed after Eq. (4.21).

Exercise 4.22: Check that the currents conserve overall flow of particles, that is $j_+ + j_- = j_B$. In effect, the *net* flow of current to the right before and after the step is the same. Show that the transmission coefficient for particle flow into the potential step is $j_B/j_+ = 4kk''/(k + k'')^2$.

Tunnelling of waves can be seen in optics. Inside a medium, when light is incident on a surface at an angle to its normal greater than the critical angle, it is totally internally reflected. See the marked light ray in Fig. 4.5(a); the middle ray is also beyond the critical angle whereas the upper ray is above the angle and is partially reflected and partially transmitted into the other block of perspex. In the totally internally reflected cases there is an ex-

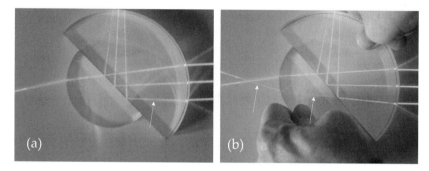

Figure 4.5: (a) Light beams incident internally on a perspex surface at just below and above the angle of critical internal reflection. (b) On reducing the air gap between the two blocks, the wave marked in (a) now tunnels through the "forbidden region" and emerges as a propagating wave in the second block, also marked. We thank Robin Hughes for help with this demonstration.

ponentially evanescent wave that penetrates the air gap between the blocks, but which does not carry energy. It is the analogue of the ψ_A wave above, which carries no particle current (Ex. 4.21). The air gap is the analogue of the forbidden region under the step. Close to the critical angle the penetration of the evanescent wave gets ever deeper. In Fig. 4.5(b) the blocks are pressed closer together, reducing the air gap in the region of the marked wave so that the evanescent wave has not so completely decayed when it approaches the other block. It again becomes a real travelling wave when it re-enters the perspex of the second block. One can see the transmitted energy of the new wave. This tunnelling through a a forbidden region where there is evanescence is treated for quantum mechanical particles in Ex. 4.25 below.

4.5 Summary

In the problems of the first three chapters, all the wavefunctions can be chosen to be purely real. However, for a complete description wavefunctions are in general complex. We have introduced complex numbers, which obey the usual rules of algebra with the extra proviso that $i^2 = -1$. We noted that the classical harmonic oscillator possesses complex exponential solutions. These are directly related to the trigonometrical solutions via Euler's identity $e^{i\theta} = \cos\theta + i\sin\theta$.

With the machinery of complex numbers, we returned to the foundations of quantum mechanics and motivated the wavefunction as a means to generate a probability distribution via the double slit experiment. We generalised the classical definition of expectation value of a quantity to the quantum version involving the expectation value of operators. Following de Broglie and Schrödinger's insights, we demonstrated the momentum operator takes the form

$$\hat{p} = -i\hbar\frac{d}{dx}.$$

The eigenstates of the momentum operator are plane waves, which carry net particle or probability flux. We found the probability flux/current in various unbound potential problems. Further, we saw that in order to have current flow and thus to discuss dynamics, we must have complex wavefunctions for the current to be non-zero.

4.6 Additional problems

Exercise 4.23: Superfluid helium may be described by the wavefunction $\psi(x) = \sqrt{n}e^{i\alpha(x)}$, where n is the superfluid density and the phase $\alpha(x)$ is a real function of position. If the density is constant, explain how the flow is related to $\frac{d\alpha}{dx}$.

Exercise 4.24: A beam of particles of energy E is incident on a square potential well with $V = 0$ for x in 0 to a, while $V = V_0$ otherwise; see Fig. 4.6(A). Show that for certain values of E there is no reflected beam. Compare this result with the classical in Ex. 1.2. *Sketch the transmission coefficient as a function of E. (This is a problem in atomic physics — the Ramsauer effect where the transmission of electrons through a vapour of neutral atoms depends on the incident electrons' energy, that is on wavelength.)

Exercise 4.25: * A beam of particles of energy E is incident on a square potential barrier of height $V = V_0$ for x in 0 to a, while $V = 0$ otherwise; see

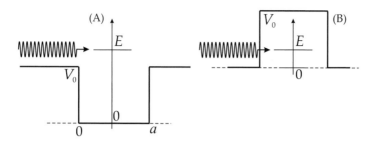

Figure 4.6: Free particle waves from $x < 0$ impinging on (A) a potential well of depth V_0. Energy is measured upwards from the bottom of the well, with the total energy E as marked. (B) A potential barrier of height V_0. For convenience energy is measured upwards from the base level of the barrier. Total energy E is shown less than V_0, but $E > V_0$ is also interesting.

Fig. 4.6(B). Specify the 5 wavefunctions involved in this problem in the case of $E < V_0$. Remember that since the barrier is of finite thickness, unlike the step, the component $e^{+k'x}$ cannot be neglected — such waves are generated by reflection from the back face of the barrier. Show that the modulus squared of the emergent wave function is

$$|T|^2 = \frac{4k^2k'^2}{\sinh^2(k'a)(k^2 + k'^2)^2} \approx \frac{16k^2k'^2e^{-2k'a}}{(k^2 + k'^2)^2} \approx e^{-2k'a},$$

the latter two forms holding when $k'a \gg 1$. Calculate the flux of particles passing through the classically forbidden region of the barrier. This process whereby particles pass through the classically forbidden region is called *tunnelling*. [The k and k' are defined as in Fig. 4.4(A), that is k for the classically allowed regions, k' for the forbidden region inside the barrier.]

Exercise 4.26: In the case of weak tunnelling ($k'a \gg 1$), what is the ratio of the probabilities of two successive electrons to that of a single particle with twice the mass of an electron tunnelling through the same barrier?

Exercise 4.27: A 1-D model of an uranium nucleus undergoing radioactive alpha decay is an alpha particle trapped within a potential well shown in Fig. 4.7 with energy $E_\alpha < V_0$. Two protons and two neutrons (an nascent alpha particle) form a particularly stable combination of nucleons, which can be considered as moving together within uranium nucleus. The well

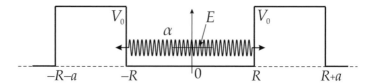

Figure 4.7: A 1-D model well for an alpha particle of energy E within a uranium nucleus of radius R that presents a barrier of height V_0 for the α to tunnel through.

is the combination of the strong nuclear force trapping the nucleons inside the nucleus and the electrostatic force trying to break it apart. Suppose before the uranium decays, the alpha particle travels *classically* back and forth between $-R$ and $+R$, with the radius of the nucleus $R = 8.8$ fm. What is the number of times per second it hits the edge of the nucleus if alpha particle has energy $E_\alpha = 4.3$ MeV and mass of 3.7 GeV/c^2? Making use of the result of Ex. 4.25 with $V_0 = 30$ MeV and $a = 20$ fm, what is the probability per collision with the nuclear edge for the alpha particle to escape the nucleus by tunnelling, and thus, what is the probability of the uranium decaying in a second? Is this consistent with the ^{238}U half-life of 1.4×10^{17} s?

Exercise 4.28: Alpha particles have typical energies 2–8 MeV (a factor of four difference in range) upon emission from an alpha radiactive decay. Using the model of Ex. 4.27 with a potential barrier of height 30 MeV and width 20 fm, explain how the observed half-lives of radionuclides span from microseconds to hundreds of billion years (a factor of 10^{24}!).

Exercise 4.29: The particles incident on the square potential barrier of Fig. 4.6 (B) now have $E > V_0$. Calculate the flux of particles passing the barrier as a multiple of the incident flux. Comment on how the transmission varies with energy. [Some special cases of transmission have optical analogies that are exploited in high performance lenses.]

5

Quantum dynamics and higher spatial dimensions

Higher spatial dimensions, partial differentiation, time evolution, connection with energy, travelling waves

We have conspicuously only attacked problems in one spatial dimension. The essential nature of quantum mechanics was revealed by these restricted problems — localisation kinetic energy, penetration into regions of negative kinetic energy, the role of phase, and the connection between wavefunction curvature and energy. We now explore two and higher dimensional motion and potentials, that is potentials $V(x, y, \dots)$ depending on more than one independent (here spatial) variable. Likewise momentum will be a vector with more than one component: $\boldsymbol{p} = (p_x, p_y, \dots)$.

How does a quantum system evolve in time? It will turn out that the conjugate variable to time is energy, just as that conjugate to space was momentum. The pairing of variables as conjugates is fundamental to quantum mechanics, see §1.1. One cannot know them both simultaneously except within the bounds of accuracy given by the uncertainty principle. Likewise, just as p was related to space by a derivative ($\hat{p} \propto \mathrm{d}/\mathrm{d}x$), so will E and t be related. The connection between conjugate variables also has other deep aspects.

As we have hinted, energy gives an operator $\propto \mathrm{d}/\mathrm{d}t$ and we find that the time-dependent Schrödinger equation has at least two independent variables, x and t, giving us a $\psi(x, t)$. Or in a 2-D spatial problem, even the time-independent Schrödinger equation has two independent variables x, y

giving a $\psi(x,y)$. Before we can proceed with these two final problems, we have our final mathematical preliminary — the generalisation of differentiation to where one has more than one independent variable.

5.1   Partial differentiation

Consider the Gaussian $f(x,y) = \exp(-x^2/2a^2 - y^2/2b^2)$. Fig. 5.1 shows that f is a surface in 3-D. For a given position (x,y) in the plane of the

Figure 5.1: A 2-D Gaussian $f(x,y)$ describes a surface. Trajectories along one coordinate with a fixed value of the other coordinate are shown along the surface, for instance that at a fixed y_0 with x varying through its range (heavy curve).

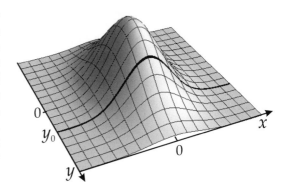

independent variables, the surface point is above it at a height of $z = f(x,y)$ (the coordinate z taking its usual Cartesian sense; here it is not a complex number!). One could take $y = y_0$ to be a constant and then inquire what is the slope of the path on the surface parallel to the x axis at this fixed y_0. One has

$$f(x,y_0) = e^{-y_0^2/2b^2}.e^{-x^2/2a^2}$$

where one can think of the prefactor $e^{-y_0^2/2b^2}$ as simply a constant number along the curve. Then $f(x,y_0) \propto e^{-x^2/2a^2}$ is just a 1-D Gaussian, in x, and is even in its standard form. Its magnitude is scaled by $e^{-y_0^2/2b^2}$ which we have suppressed while highlighting the x dependence. The slope of the surface along this curve is

$$\frac{df}{dx}\bigg|_{y_0} = e^{-y_0^2/2b^2}.\left(-\frac{x}{a^2}.e^{-x^2/2a^2}\right), \tag{5.1}$$

where the $\big|_{y_0}$ emphasises we have treated y_0 as a constant in differentiating with respect to x (sometimes written $)_{y_0}$). Derivatives with respect to one independent variable, keeping the other(s) fixed, are called *partial derivatives* and are written $\partial f/\partial x$. The partial symbol ∂ is reserved for this purpose. Sometimes the variable(s) being kept constant is recorded for clarity; here it would be $\partial f/\partial x|_y$. Note the $_0$ on the y is not needed.

Note the partial derivative $\frac{\partial f}{\partial x} = -\frac{x}{a^2}\exp(-x^2/2a^2 - y^2/2b^2)$ is nevertheless a function of y. We fix y when taking the derivative with respect to x, but the value for the resulting slope in the x direction does depend on y; see Fig. 5.1. For instance, the x curve on the surface for $y = 0$ passes over the summit and the slope as we go down will be greater than if our line at constant $y \neq 0$ took us across the flanks of the hill, as shown in the figure. We have chosen as an illustration a separable f, that is, where the x and y dependence separates. But this is not necessary, as examples now show.

Exercise 5.1: What is $\partial r/\partial x$, where $r = \sqrt{x^2 + y^2 + z^2}$ is the modulus of the vector $r = (x, y, z)$ from the origin in 3-D?

Solution: $\frac{\partial r}{\partial x} = \frac{x}{\sqrt{x^2+y^2+z^2}}$ on differentiating the square root with respect to its argument $x^2 + y^2 + z^2$, and then differentiating the argument with respect to x. See Ex. 1.10 for the use of the chain rule when differentiating a function of a function. Check one can write the answer as $\partial r/\partial x = x/r$.

Exercise 5.2: The Coulomb electrical energy of interaction between two charges Q and q separated by a distance r is $U = qQ/(4\pi\epsilon_0 r)$. Evaluate the force in the y direction, $f_y = -\partial U/\partial y$.

Solution: $f_y = qQy/(4\pi\epsilon_0 r^3)$.

Force is a vector with components as given above and can be written as

$$f = (f_x, f_y, f_z) = -\left(\frac{\partial U}{\partial x}, \frac{\partial U}{\partial y}, \frac{\partial U}{\partial z}\right).$$

Such a vector of derivatives is usually written as $f = -\nabla U$, where the operator $\nabla \equiv \left(\frac{\partial}{\partial x}, \frac{\partial}{\partial y}, \frac{\partial}{\partial z}\right)$ is known as "grad" (for gradient operator) and is not just applied to gradients of potentials.

Integration in more than 1-D

A related process is of course integration, for example in 2-D. The volume under the surface $z = f(x, y)$ is the multiple integral

$$V = \iint f(x, y)\, dx\, dy.$$

The integrations with respect to each variable can be done in any order if there is absolute convergence, the as yet undone variables being constant as the integrals earlier in the sequence are executed. For example, the double integral $\int_0^R \int_0^R xy\sqrt{x^2+y^2}\,dx\,dy$ is first attacked by separating off the constant y pieces and performing $\int_0^R \sqrt{x^2+y^2}x\,dx = \frac{1}{3}(x^2+y^2)^{3/2}\Big|_0^R = \frac{1}{3}\left[(R^2+y^2)^{3/2}-y^3\right]$. Integrating this result times y (y being the piece previously detached), one obtains $2(2\sqrt{2}-1)R^5/15$. The reader is urged to check the integrations, if necessary by differentiating the result to return to the starting point, and to complete the step to the final answer.

5.2   Further postulates of quantum mechanics

Now that we have the mathematical machinery to tackle more that one dimension, we are able to complete our listing of the postulates of quantum mechanics from §2.2 and discuss their consequences.

Postulate 1 The state of a quantum mechanical system is completely specified by a complex function $\psi(x,t)$, that depends on the position x of the particle and on time t. This function is called the wavefunction.

Postulate 2 The wavefunction has the property that $|\psi(x)|^2 d^3x$ is the probability that the particle lies in a cube of size $d^3x = dxdydz$ centred at x. This assumes the wavefunction is normalised so that the total probability is unity: $\int|\psi(x)|^2 d^3x = 1$.

Postulate 3 To every observable or measurable quantity A in classical mechanics, there corresponds a linear Hermitian[1] operator $\hat{A}$ in quantum mechanics.

Postulate 4 The result of any measurement of observable A can only be one of the eigenvalues a of the associated operator $\hat{A}$, which satisfy the eigenvalue equation

$$\hat{A}\psi_a = a\psi_a,$$

where ψ_a is the eigenfunction of $\hat{A}$ corresponding to the eigenvalue a. The eigenvalue is guaranteed to be real since $\hat{A}$ is Hermitian.

---

[1]Loosely, Hermitian means an operator that is its own complex conjugate.

Postulate 5 If a particle is in a state described by ψ, then the probability[2] of obtaining the value a in a measurement of observable A is given by

$$p(a) = \left| \int \psi_a^* \psi \, d^3 x \right|^2 .$$

Postulate 6 After a measurement of A where the result a is found, the wavefunction of the system becomes the corresponding eigenfunction ψ_a. This is called the *collapse of the wavefunction*.

Postulate 7 Between measurements, the wavefunction evolves in time according to the time dependent Schrödinger equation

$$-\frac{\hbar^2}{2m}\left(\frac{\partial^2 \psi}{\partial x^2} + \frac{\partial^2 \psi}{\partial x^2} + \frac{\partial^2 \psi}{\partial x^2}\right) + V(x)\psi = i\hbar\frac{\partial \psi}{\partial t}.$$

5.3 Potentials in higher dimensions

The time-independent Schrödinger equation is $(\hat{T} + V)\psi = E\psi$ where $\hat{T} = \hat{p}^2/2m$. Now we have motion in more than one direction. Thus $\boldsymbol{p} = (p_x, p_y, p_z)$ is a vector, and the magnitude squared of the momentum is $p^2 = \boldsymbol{p} \cdot \boldsymbol{p} = p_x^2 + p_y^2 + p_z^2$. The kinetic energy operator will be

$$\hat{T} = \frac{1}{2m}\left(\hat{p}_x^2 + \hat{p}_y^2 + \hat{p}_z^2\right) \rightarrow -\frac{\hbar^2}{2m}\left(\frac{\partial^2}{\partial x^2} + \frac{\partial^2}{\partial y^2} + \frac{\partial^2}{\partial z^2}\right), \quad (5.2)$$

where we retain operator definitions such as $\hat{p} = -i\hbar d/dx$ but differentiate appropriately because there is more than one independent variable.

2-D infinite square well potential

Consider a potential $V = 0$ inside the square area where $x \in [0, a]$ and $y \in [0, a]$, with $V = \infty$ outside. We no longer have a confining slab, that is confinement just along x, with y, z free. Now y motion is also limited. The Schrödinger equation in the finite region is

$$-\frac{\hbar^2}{2m}\left(\frac{\partial^2 \psi}{\partial x^2} + \frac{\partial^2 \psi}{\partial y^2}\right) = E\psi. \quad (5.3)$$

---

[2]Assuming normalised wavefunctions.

This equation looks formidable at first sight. But it is a simple equation, susceptible to the same analysis we have already done in 1-D. A few examples will give confidence that this assertion is true! Take a guess wavefunction $\psi \propto \sin(k_x x) \sin(k_y y)$. The labels on the wavevectors simply mean the wavevector for that particular direction, x or y. The choice ensures that $\psi = 0$ at the edges with $x = 0$ or $y = 0$ since $\sin(0) = 0$. We also want $\psi = 0$ along $x = a$ and $y = a$, which is assured by taking $k_x = l\pi/a$ and $k_y = n\pi/a$ for integers l and n (as in 1-D problems). But is the ψ a solution of the Schrödinger equation? We try our guess out and obtain

$$\frac{\hbar^2}{2m} \left(k_x^2 + k_y^2 \right) \psi = E\psi. \tag{5.4}$$

We have a solution if the energy takes the eigenvalue $E_{ln} = \frac{\hbar^2 \pi^2}{2ma^2} \left(l^2 + n^2 \right)$. As in Eq. (5.2) where the quadratic terms in p were additive in the energy, so here the energy contributions from the eigenfunctions in the different directions also add. The problem is just as before, but with 2 labels for eigenstates rather than 1. For the wavefunction we could have taken other combinations such as sin.cos, cos.sin, cos.cos, $e^i.e^i$, $e^i.cos$ etc. so the functions, when twice differentiated, give a multiple of their starting form (thus our guess was not so wild). Note that ψ is just a *product* of an x wavefunction times a y wavefunction. The effect in the Schrödinger equation was to give *additions* of separate contributions. This kind of solution is called *separable*, and frequently occurs in physics. The particular choice to make from the above list of possible solutions is determined by boundary conditions. Sometimes separability fails because of the form of the potential $V(x, y, z)$, but this can mostly be circumvented by a change of coordinate system.

Exercise 5.3: Normalised, ψ would be written $A_{ln} \sin(l\pi x/a) \sin(n\pi y/a)$. Show that the normalising constant is $A_{ln} = 2/a$.

Exercise 5.4: Consider an infinite square well potential with $V = 0$ in the rectangle where x is in 0 to a and y is in 0 to b, with $a \neq b$. What are the wavefunctions, including their normalisation? Show that the eigen energies are $E_{ln} = \frac{\hbar^2 \pi^2}{2m} \left[(l/a)^2 + (n/b)^2 \right]$.

Free and bound motion together — nanowires

Fine wires with nanometre cross sections constrain electrons to transverse bound states while allowing free motion along their length. Such nanowires are important in advanced semiconductor devices. The simplest model is to consider a 1-D infinite square well: electrons are confined to an x-interval, 0 to a, where $V = 0$. In the y direction, the long axis of the trench, motion is free; see Fig. 5.2. Clearly wavefunctions must be of a separable form as

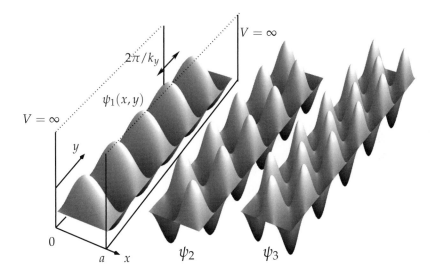

Figure 5.2: An infinite square well potential in the x direction extended indefinitely to allow free motion in the y direction. The ground state wavefunction, ψ_1, is shown in the well (the real part of the free-particle state in the y direction is depicted, with y periodicity $2\pi/k_y$ indicated). The equivalent plots for ψ_2 and ψ_3 are shown without the well for clarity.

they are for Eq. (5.3). In this case they are $\psi(x,y) \propto \sin(k_x x)e^{ik_y y}$, that is (localised)×(free). The transverse requirement of vanishing of the wavefunction at $x = 0$ is assured by the choice of sine, and at $x = a$ is assured by the usual choice $k_x \to k_n = n\pi/a$. In the Schrödinger equation (5.3) we accordingly have, from an equivalence to (5.4),

$$E = \frac{\hbar^2}{2m}\left(\left(\frac{n\pi}{a}\right)^2 + k_y^2\right) \equiv E_n + \hbar^2 k_y^2/2m\,, \tag{5.5}$$

where E_n is the nth state energy of the 1-D square well potential. The eigenfunction $\psi_1(x,y)$ corresponding to $n = 1$ is shown in Fig. 5.2. The simple

$\sin(\pi x/a)$ transverse form is modulated longitudinally by the $e^{ik_y y}$ variation, the real or imaginary part being depicted. When $n = 2, 3, \ldots$ the wavefunctions $\psi_2, \psi_3, \ldots$ have $1, 2, \ldots$ internal nodes in the transverse direction. There is strong similarity between these wave solutions and those for guided electromagnetic waves and for sound in a tube.

From Eq. (5.5), the electron's y-momentum (along the channel) is $\hbar k_y = \sqrt{2m(E - E_n)}$. The energy-momentum or energy-wavevector connection $E(k_y)$ is known as the dispersion relation in physics. Here it is not of the classical type, but has a gap, E_n, due to transverse (x) quantisation; see Fig. 5.3. The energy values in Fig. 5.3 at $k_y = 0$, that is no variation along

Figure 5.3: Energy $E(k_y)$ dependent on wavevector $k_y \equiv p_y/\hbar$ for electrons in the $n = 1$ eigenstate moving along a nano-wire. There is an offset, E_1, of the energy from zero for the $k_y = 0$ state (known as a gap). A free electron $E(k_y)$ by comparison shows no gap.

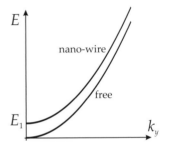

the y direction, are just those in Fig. 2.5(a), on page 46. For each of those levels here the energy rises with $k_y > 0$ due to additional kinetic energy associated with the y motion. The levels are no longer sharp as in Fig. 2.5(a). In fact there are bands of allowed energies which betray the geometry the particles explore.

Exercise 5.5: Calculate the eigen energies and eigenfunctions for a narrow wire modelled as a rectangular infinite square well potential in the x–y plane, where $x \in [0, a]$ and $y \in [0, b]$ define a region with $V = 0$, continuing in the z extension of this rectangle.

Solution: $E = E_{ln} + \hbar^2 k_z^2/2m$ where $E_{ln} = \frac{\hbar^2}{2m}\left(\left(\frac{l\pi}{a}\right)^2 + \left(\frac{n\pi}{b}\right)^2\right)$.

2-D free motion with a 1-D step

We consider the oblique incidence of a matter wave onto a step. One can have the curious phenomenon that the region of the step might not be forbidden for normal incidence, but becomes so with obliquity — a form of total external reflection, to modify a phrase from optics, that we have seen in the 1-D step problem, Ex. 4.21. We must now deal with waves travelling

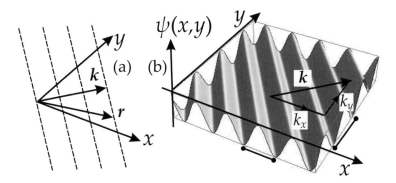

Figure 5.4: A wave oblique to the x and y axes. The lines of constant phase are perpendicular to the wavevector k. (a) Spatial points r on a line of constant phase share the same projection, $r \cdot k$, along k. (b) The form of the wave. Note advancing from crest to crest along the coordinate axes involves the longer distances $2\pi/k_x$ and $2\pi/k_y$, marked with bars, than along the normal k.

in 2-D: consider a motion with $p = \hbar k = \hbar(k_x, k_y)$ at an angle θ_i to the x axis. Such oblique incidence is shown in Figs. 5.4 and 5.5. The wavevector k is normal to the planes or lines, depending on the wave, of constant phase. Figure 5.4(a) shows lines of constant phase with perpendicular vector k. All points r on the line are advanced by the same phase from the equivalent line going through the origin. They must have the same component along k, that is $r \cdot k = $ const. (Recall the definition Eq.(1.49) of the dot product as a projection which means here the component of distance r along k must be a constant.) Thus all such points share the same phase, $r \cdot k$. A component of distance along k of the wavelength λ sees the phase advance by 2π, for instance going from crest to crest as in Fig. 5.4(b), whereupon one again sees that k has magnitude $2\pi/\lambda$.[3]

In Fig. 5.5, for clarity the wavevectors alone are shown for the wave as it is thus incident, reflected and transmitted at the step. The incident wavefunction in region A is $\psi \propto e^{i(k_x x + k_y y)}$, and the reflected one has the

---

[3]It is easy to consider travelling waves at this point too: let $r \cdot k - \omega t = $ const where ω is a constant with the units of frequency so that ωt is dimensionless. It must mean that the points r on the lines of constant phase must be increasing their projection on to k as $\omega t/k$ in order to keep $r \cdot k - \omega t$ constant. Thus $\omega t/k$ must be ct where $c = \omega/k$ is the phase velocity of the travelling wave. Comparison with $c = \nu\lambda$ with ν the frequency shows that $\omega = 2\pi\nu$ is the usual angular frequency. Thus plane waves are of the form $\sin(k \cdot r - \omega t)$ in more than one dimension.

Figure 5.5: The wavevector k_i of a wave obliquely incident, with angle of incidence θ_i, from A onto a step (region B) rising sharply with x and extending along the y direction. The transmitted wave, with k_t, has an angle of transmission θ_t. The parallel components of the wavevector, k_y, are the same in all three vector triangles. The transmitted wave vector's normal component is shortened to k'_x from the incident and reflected k_x, thereby leading to refraction.

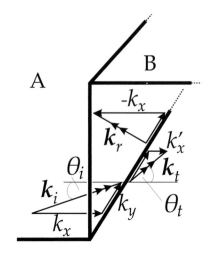

x component of its wavevector (and hence its momentum) reversed, that is $\psi \propto e^{i(-k_x x + k_y y)}$, while k_y remains the same. The vector triangles in A of the figure thus show that the angles of incidence and reflection are the same. The ratios of the values of k_x to k_y are determined by the angle of incidence. From the vector triangle for the incident wavevector in Fig. 5.5, one has $\tan \theta_i = k_y/k_x$ or equivalently and $k_y = k \sin \theta_i$ where k is the modulus of the incident wavevector $k_i = k(\cos \theta_i, \sin \theta_i)$; see Fig. 5.4.

The wavefunctions are

Region A $\qquad\qquad \psi_A = A_+ e^{i(k_x x + k_y y)} + A_- e^{i(-k_x x + k_y y)}$

Region B $\qquad\qquad \psi_B = B e^{i(k'_x x + k_y y)}$ or $B e^{-k''_x x + i k_y y}$,

where A_+ and A_- respectively weight the incident and reflected waves. The transmitted waves, weighted by B, are either oscillatory with $e^{i k'_x x}$, or decaying with $e^{-k''_x x}$, depending on the effective energy. The ψs taken have the *same* y-variation, that is $e^{i k_y y}$, on each side of the step so that ψ_A and ψ_B (and their derivatives $\partial \psi / \partial x$) can be matched at $x = 0$ for *all* y. Both the choice of function (e^i) and the value of k_y must be the same on each side to achieve this matching all along the interface. The energies corresponding to these ks are

Region A $\qquad E = \dfrac{\hbar^2}{2m}\left(k_x^2 + k_y^2\right) \equiv \dfrac{\hbar^2}{2m}k^2$ $\qquad$ (for both $\pm k_x$) (5.6)

Region B $\qquad E = \dfrac{\hbar^2}{2m}\left(k_x'^2 + k_y^2\right) + V_0$ $\qquad$ (propagating in B) (5.7)

$\qquad\qquad E = \dfrac{\hbar^2}{2m}\left(-k_x''^2 + k_y^2\right) + V_0$ $\qquad$ (evanescent in B). (5.8)

The kinetic energy is seen in Eq. (5.6) to be of the usual form $T = \frac{\hbar^2}{2m}k^2$, with k the modulus of the wavevector that describes the phase variation along the normal to the wave crests; Fig. 5.4.

For *normal* incidence, if the incident energy E is greater than the step height V_0, then we have seen wave propagation into the step; see Fig. 4.4. For oblique incidence, even if $E > V_0$, we may not get penetration into the step since some of the kinetic energy is taken up by the $\hbar^2 k_y^2/2m$ term in Eq. (5.6) associated with motion parallel to the step's face. Equating the expressions for E in Eqs. (5.6) and (5.7), or in Eqs. (5.6) and (5.8), depending on k_x, gives

$$k_x'^2 = k_x^2 - \frac{2mV_0}{\hbar^2} \qquad \text{for } k_x > \sqrt{\frac{2mV_0}{\hbar^2}}$$

$$k_x''^2 = \frac{2mV_0}{\hbar^2} - k_x^2 \qquad \text{for } k_x < \sqrt{\frac{2mV_0}{\hbar^2}}.$$

Whether we get transmission into or evanescence (exponential decay) in the step depends on whether the kinetic energy associated with the normal (x) component of the motion of approach to the step, $\hbar^2 k_x^2/2m$, is greater or less respectively than the step height V_0.

Exercise 5.6: For transmission into the step, derive the angle of refraction in terms of the angle of incidence, and the step height in relation to the incident energy: $\tan^2\theta_t = \tan^2(\theta_i)/(1 - \sec^2(\theta_i)V_0/E)$.

Ex. 5.6 reveals a very interesting general property of waves at interfaces. At an angle of incidence such that $\sec^2\theta_i = E/V_0$, the denominator of the above expression for $\tan\theta_t$ vanishes and the right hand side diverges. That means $\theta_t \to \pi/2$. The refracted wave is along the interface — there no real transmission any more. Evanescence sets in, and reflection becomes total. In optics it is total internal reflection at a critical angle of incidence given in terms of the refractive indices of the two media. Here is it total *external* reflection at an angle $\theta_c = \tan^{-1}\sqrt{\frac{E-V_0}{V_0}}$.

Exercise 5.7: *By considering the wavefunction matching conditions (i) and (ii) on page 51, derive an expression for the reflection coefficient of the wave as a function of energy and angle of incidence.

The flux j is now a vector. Check that j_x is the same for $x < 0$ and $x > 0$ for transmission, and vanishes in both regions for evanescence.

Distributed oscillators — quantising the oscillations of a string

Reconsider a string of length L, with tension T and mass μ per unit length. Before quantising its motion, one must first understand its classical motion; the standing waves of Sect. 1.2 are the envelope of the string's transverse oscillations. Consider the motion of a section of string in Fig. 5.6. A small section between x and $x + dx$ (of mass μdx) is shown with tan-

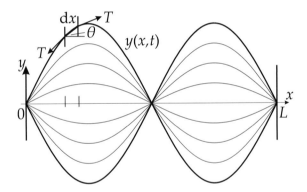

Figure 5.6: A stretched string under tension. The transverse displacement y is a function of position x, where x varies from 0 to L, and of time t. The standing wave form y_1, the first excited state (with one internal node), is shown (heavy lines) at the two extremes of its motion. Intermediate states are shown in lighter lines.

gential tension forces acting at each end, the tangents having angles $\theta(x)$ and $\theta(x + dx)$. For small angles θ one has $\sin\theta \approx \tan\theta$. The vertical component of force is $T\sin\theta$ and the net vertical force on the interval is the difference between the values of $T\sin\theta$ at its ends. This difference is $dxTd(\sin\theta)/dx \approx dxTd(\tan\theta)/dx$, see Eq. (1.38). But $\tan\theta = dy/dx$ and thus this difference is $\mathrm{d}xT\mathrm{d}^2y/\mathrm{d}x^2$. We set this equal to mass $\times$ acceleration for this element of string $\mu\mathrm{d}x\partial^2y/\partial t^2$. We now need partial derivatives because we are considering more than one independent variable, here x and t. Equating these influences and cancelling the lengths $\mathrm{d}x$ we obtain

$$\mu\frac{\partial^2 y}{\partial t^2} = T\frac{\partial^2 y}{\partial x^2}. \qquad (5.9)$$

This equation describes waves on a string that have wave speed $\sqrt{T/\mu}$. The spatial dependence must be sinusoidal: a separable solution of Eq. (5.9) is $y(x,t) = y_m(t)\sin(k_m x)$ since $\partial^2 y/\partial x^2$ gives back $-k_m^2\sin(k_m x)$. One then has a chance of matching the form of the left hand side of Eq. (5.9), and the choice of sine rather than cosine ensured that $y = 0$ at $x = 0$ at all times. Clearly $y = 0$ at $x = L$ demands discrete values $k_m = m\pi/L$ (check indeed $\sin(k_m x) = 0$ at that point). The y_m contains the t dependence that we must now determine. Put this $y(x,t)$ back into Eq. (5.9) to obtain

$$\frac{\mathrm{d}^2 y_m}{\mathrm{d}t^2} = -c^2 k_m^2 y_m. \qquad (5.10)$$

To get this equation, we have cancelled off each side the $\sin(k_m x)$ factor. The $-k_m^2$ factor on the right hand side came from $\partial^2/\partial x^2$ acting on the $\sin(k_m x)$ function before it was cancelled. Note that in Eq. (5.10) we are back to simple derivatives since we only have t to consider from now on. The c^2 simply writes the T/μ term. If we write $c^2 k_m^2$ as ω_m^2 then we have an equation formally just like our SHM Eqs. (1.26) and (3.10)

$$\frac{\mathrm{d}^2 y_m}{\mathrm{d}t^2} = -\omega_m^2 y_m \qquad (5.11)$$

even though it corresponds to the distributed system of Fig. 5.6 and not to the simple harmonic motion of a point particle. We can now quantise the oscillations of the mth mode in the same way as we did the harmonic oscillator in §3.2 on page 56. The energy associated with the motion of the normal mode m has energy $E_n^{(m)} = (n + \frac{1}{2})\hbar\omega_m$ which corresponds to n quanta each of energy $\hbar\omega_m$ in the state. Each quantum oscillator has a different fundamental frequency $\omega_m = \sqrt{\frac{T}{\mu}}m\pi/L$ depending on its spatial character, that is the choice of k_m, but that is all that survives of the spatial nature of the problem when considering Eq. (5.11).

The procedure we have sketched above for the quantisation of the string is that employed in *quantum field theory*. In 1926, Born, Heisenberg and

Jordan applied this method to the electromagnetic field. They found that constraining the field to vanish at the boundaries of a cavity, it behaved like the sum of independent harmonic oscillators with angular frequency $\omega_m = m\pi c/L$ like the string. Each k-mode could be occupied by certain numbers of quanta called *photons* by Einstein. The same can be done for any field or wave. For example, phonons are quantised sound waves, electrons are quantised Dirac fields, ...

5.4   The dynamics of quantum states

To find the operator that might describe time evolution, we return to de Broglie for inspiration, as we did at the start of Chapter 4. The quantum mechanics of electromagnetic radiation showed that energy E and frequency ν are related by

$$E = h\nu \quad \text{or} \quad E = \hbar\omega \tag{5.12}$$

(using also the more normal connection with angular frequency ω). Free travelling waves would be, extending our ideas of free particle states in Chapter 4, of the form $\psi \propto e^{i(kx-\omega t)}$. We want an operator for E to give an equation like $\hat{H}\psi = E\psi$ where E is the eigenvalue of the operator $\hat{H}$. One can see by explicit differentiation that $\hat{H}\psi \equiv (i\hbar\partial/\partial t)\,\psi$ will do that job and provide $E = \hbar\omega$ (5.12). We therefore postulate for the energy operator

$$\hat{H} = i\hbar\frac{\partial}{\partial t}, \tag{5.13}$$

which is one of the starting points of quantum mechanics in parallel with the definition (4.14) for the momentum operator. See postulate 7, page 89. Then the Schrödinger equation $\left(\hat{T} + V(x)\right)\psi = \hat{H}\psi$ is

$$\boxed{i\hbar\frac{\partial\psi}{\partial t} = -\frac{\hbar^2}{2m}\frac{\partial^2\psi}{\partial x^2} + V(x)\psi} \tag{5.14}$$

where $\partial^2\psi/\partial x^2$ is understood to be extended to $\partial^2\psi/\partial x^2 + \partial^2\psi/\partial y^2 + \dots$ if we are describing motion in higher spatial dimensions.

This equation is called the *time-dependent Schrödinger equation*.

We recover the time-independent form studied hitherto by writing

$$\psi(x,t) = \psi(x)e^{-i\omega t} \equiv \psi(x)e^{-i(E/\hbar)t}. \tag{5.15}$$

The two ψ functions, distinguished by the form of their arguments, are respectively the time-dependent and time-independent wavefunctions. Injecting $\psi(x,t)$ into (5.14) yields the expected $E\psi(x) = -(\hbar^2/2m)d^2\psi/dx^2$

since the $e^{-i(E/\hbar)t}$ left behind after $i\hbar\partial/\partial t$ then cancels on each side. The surviving $\psi(x)$ is a function of x, needing only normal derivatives d^2/dx^2.

We now have the fully time-dependent states of a quantum system. For instance in the infinite well case we have

$$\psi_n(x,t) = A_n e^{-i(E_n/\hbar)t} \sin\left(\frac{n\pi x}{a}\right) \equiv e^{-i(E_n/\hbar)t}\psi_n(x).$$

You should confirm that

$$|\psi_n(x,t)|^2 = \psi_n^*(x,t)\psi_n(x,t) = \psi_n^2(x) = A_n^2 \sin^2\left(\frac{n\pi x}{a}\right)$$

since $\left|e^{-i(E_n/\hbar)t}\right|^2 = 1$. The time dependence is entirely in a time-dependent phase factor with a modulus of 1.

One might reasonably ask is it ever then feasible to see dynamical effects in quantum mechanics since physical observations manifest themselves via $|\psi_n(x,t)|^2$ and from this the factor $e^{-i(E/\hbar)t}$ carrying the time-dependence has vanished? The answer is yes, for several reasons.

(i) We discussed above eigenstates of the energy operator which are very special since this operator determines time dependence. If the system is in a superposed state of the Hamiltonian $\hat{H}$, let us say $\psi(x) = c_1\psi_1(x) + c_2\psi_2(x)$ at time $t = 0$, it is not in an eigenstate of $\hat{H}$, even if the component states ψ_1 and ψ_2 *are* eigenstates; see the discussion on page 75, and Exs. 4.15 & 4.16, where conditions on the weights c_1 and c_2 are given. Now there is a non-trivial time dependence

$$\psi(x,t) = c_1\psi_1(x)e^{-i(E_1/\hbar)t} + c_2\psi_2(x)e^{-i(E_2/\hbar)t} \tag{5.16}$$

and one finds that observables of the system vary in time; see Ex. 5.8. If we have an eigenstate, all expectation values are "stationary", that is, are constant in time.

(ii) We have considered the closely related operators $\hat{H}$ and $\hat{p}$. Other physical variables have different operators associated with them and different resultant eigenstates. Eigenstates of other operators will generally be sums of the energy eigenstates and therefore have a non-trivial time-dependence; see Ex. 5.8 for an explicit example.

To explore more dynamics we need further physical variables other than energy, position etc., matters delayed to higher courses in quantum mechanics.

Exercise 5.8: *A the particle confined to an infinite square well of width a is in an equal mixture of the ground and first excited states, ψ_1 and ψ_2. Show that the mean square position $\langle x^2 \rangle$ associated with $\psi(x,t)$ is:

$$\langle x^2 \rangle = \frac{1}{2} \left(\langle x^2 \rangle_1 + \langle x^2 \rangle_2 \right) - \left(\frac{4}{3\pi} \right)^2 a^2 \cos \left(\frac{E_2 - E_1}{\hbar} t \right). \qquad (5.17)$$

Here $\langle x^2 \rangle_1$ is the mean square expected for state 1, and analogously for 2. The first terms are what one might naïvely expect, that is the weighted sum of the individual results. The second gives a complicated time evolution. Ex. 1.15 is useful for this problem.

We conclude with a word about waves. Functions like $\sin(kx - \omega t)$ are travelling wave solutions of a classical wave equation[4], which is second order in its time derivative. By contrast the time-dependent Schrödinger equation (5.14) is only *first* order in its time derivative and hence $\partial/\partial t$ would only take sine to cosine and not back again to sine as required for a solution. One must, to have wave solutions to Eq. (5.14), take $e^{i(kx-\omega t)}$ which is restored to a multiple of itself when differentiated only once. Quantum travelling waves are intrinsically complex. It is their phase that gives rise to their particle flux, as we have seen in Ex. 4.23 on page 82.

5.5 Summary

In our final chapter, we were able to state the postulates of quantum mechanics fully. Using multi-variable calculus, we generalised our previous work to higher spatial dimensions and included the effects of time dependence.

After practice with the easily separable 2-D infinite well, we discussed the wave-guided motion of electrons in nanowires and their 2-D motion against an oblique step. In these cases, the motion could be decoupled into component directions.

In quantising the waves on a stretched string, we found that each harmonic or normal mode behaved exactly like a harmonic oscillator with its own characteristic frequency. The number of excitations of a given mode corresponds to a particle in quantum field theory.

---

[4]For example, $\left(\frac{1}{c^2} \frac{\partial^2}{\partial t^2} - \nabla^2 \right) \psi(x,t) = 0$.

We concluded our treatment of quantum mechanics by giving the full time dependent Schrödinger equation

$$-\frac{\hbar^2}{2m}\left(\frac{\partial^2\psi}{\partial x^2} + \frac{\partial^2\psi}{\partial x^2} + \frac{\partial^2\psi}{\partial x^2}\right) + V(x)\psi = i\hbar\frac{\partial\psi}{\partial t}$$

and its solution — a linear combination of energy eigenstates (of the time independent equation), the temporal variation of each being through a complex exponential involving its eigen energy:

$$\psi(x,t) = \sum_n c_n e^{-i(E_n/\hbar)t}\psi_n(x).$$

5.6 Outlook

This introduction to quantum mechanics has been brief to expose the reader to just the essentials of quantum theory. We have motivated the postulates, which are the starting point of any physical theory. Their consequences include the quantisation of measurable quantities, the uncertainty principle, and tunnelling of particles into classically forbidden regions. These ideas, and the mathematics encountered, will serve as a platform for further study.

We have followed Schrödinger's wave mechanics approach, but to handle problems involving angular momentum and the purely quantum mechanical property of *spin* or intrinsic angular momentum, it is more convenient to use Heisenberg's matrix viewpoint. These two approaches were joined by Dirac to give rise to the modern mathematical formalism based on the linear algebra of Hibert spaces. Later the marriage of special relativity and quantum mechanics produced *quantum field theory*, which enabled questions such as "Why are all electrons identical?" to be answered.

The theory of quantum mechanics underpins our understanding of fundamental and emergent physics. For instance, success in reproducing atomic structure has provided a deeper appreciation of chemistry. On the other length scale, our knowledge of subatomic structure and particularly nucleosynthesis has implications in cosmology.

Recent technological and material science breakthroughs have been the result of quantum physics. The semiconductor revolution has been driven by studies of electronic behaviour in solids, and lately their interaction with light, spawning semiconductor components in computers, smartphones, cameras, flat screen televisions, ... There are also macroscopic manifestations of truly quantum phenomena in lasers and, more exotically, in superconductors, where electrons travel co-operatively, with zero resistance and are perfectly diamagnetic, and in the superfluidity of helium.

5.7   Additional problems

Exercise 5.9: A particle is in the ground state of an infinite potential well of size a. If suddenly, the well doubles its size to $2a$, what is the probability that it is in the new ground state? [You may find it helpful to use the identity $\sin A \sin B = \frac{1}{2}(\cos(A - B) - \cos(A + B))$.]

Suppose we find that the particle is in the ground state, what is the probability over time that it remains in it?

Exercise 5.10: An infinite square well of width a confines a particle of mass m that its wavefunction is $\psi(x,t) = c_1 e^{-iE_1 t/\hbar}\psi_1(x,t) + c_2 e^{-iE_2 t/\hbar}\psi_2(x,t)$, where ψ_1 and ψ_2 are ground and first excited states with energies E_1 and E_2, respectively. After what time T_{rev} does the wavefunction $\psi(x, T_{rev})$ recover its initial form $\psi(x,0)$? This is known as the *quantum revival time*. Further show that the quantum revival time is $T_{rev} = \frac{4ma^2}{\pi\hbar}$ for any general state. What is the equivalent classical time?

Exercise 5.11: *Weakly confining nanowires.* A particle is confined to a finite 1-D potential such that $V = V_0$ for $-\infty < x < -a$ and $a < x < \infty$, with $V = 0$ for $-a < x < a$ where motion along y is free. Solve for the binding in its x ground state along with its free motion in y. Determine the x wavevectors for the confined and evanescent regions and also the y wavevector.

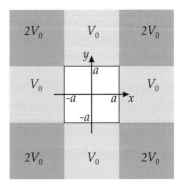

Figure 5.7: 2-D finite well: For $|x| < a$ and $|y| < a$, the potential $V = 0$. For $|x| \geqslant a$ and $|y| < a$ or for $|y| \geqslant a$ and $|x| < a$, the potential $V = V_0$. Otherwise the potential is $V = 2V_0$.

Exercise 5.12: Consider the 2-D finite well defined in Fig. 5.7 which generalises the 1-D finite potential well discussed in Chap. 3. Assuming separable forms for the ground state wavefunction in the regions with potential 0, V_0 and $2V_0$, find the ground state energy. Is there always a bound state, as in the 1-D case? Remember wavefunctions need to be matched along the boundaries of the regions of constant potential. (It suffices to find the transcendental equation analogous to Eq. (3.8) and argue graphically without finding the exact roots.) Consider also solutions with energy E such that $V_0 < E < 2V_0$. Can bound states still exist, even though there is classically enough energy to escape down a valley out to infinity? Discuss.

Exercise 5.13: Consider a particle of mass m in a 2-D harmonic potential $V(x,y) = \frac{1}{2}m\omega^2(x^2 + y^2)$. Show that Schrödinger's equation is separable (see discussion after Eq. (5.3)). Thus find solutions using 1-D results.

In 2-D or 3-D, we have extra degrees of freedom such as motion around a central point and therefore have states with angular momentum. Indeed, we use angular momentum to classify atomic orbitals, which have different characters with different angular momenta. The z-component of angular momentum is given by $L_z = xp_y - yp_x$ classically[5]. Promoting all the physical quantities to operators, we obtain the quantum mechanical equivalent

$$\hat{L}_z = \hat{x}\hat{p}_y - \hat{y}\hat{p}_x. \tag{5.18}$$

Exercise 5.14: Consider again the 2-D harmonic oscillator of Ex. 5.13. Show that the expectation value of $\hat{L}_z$ is zero for the ground state, that is, it does not possess angular momentum. Show that the wavefunction

$$\psi(x,y) \propto (u + iv)\exp(-(u^2 + v^2)/2),$$

is a solution to the Schrödinger equation (where $u = \sqrt{\frac{m\omega}{\hbar}}x$ and $v = \sqrt{\frac{m\omega}{\hbar}}y$). What is its eigen energy? How does this relate to your solutions of Ex. 5.13. Find the expectation value of $\hat{L}_z$ for this state.

Exercise 5.15: Prove there are not always bound states in 3-D. Consider the possible lowest energy states of a particle of mass m and energy E interacting with a spherical well with potential $V = 0$ for radial positions $r < a$ and $V(r) = V_0 > 0$ for $r > a$. The kinetic energy operator in spherical coordinates depends only on r if we are interested only in the lowest energy states (why is there no angular dependence?). In spherical coordinates it is

$$\hat{T} = -\frac{\hbar^2}{2m}\frac{1}{r^2}\frac{d}{dr}\left(r^2\frac{d}{dr}\right).$$

---

[5]Generally, $\mathbf{L} = \mathbf{r} \times \mathbf{p}$.

It turns out that the form of the Schrödinger equation is much simplified if we use the substitution $\psi(r) = f(r)/r$. Find the solutions $f(r)$ and hence $\psi(r)$ inside and outside $r = a$, match them together and analyse the conditions for a solution to exist.

Higher dimensions are more subtle than 1-D. By exscribing the above potential about any finite-ranged, attractive 3-D potential shows that eventually potentials can be shallow enough to lose all their bound states. But consider the final part of Ex. 5.12; even a particle of energy higher than that needed to escape in 1-D ends up being confined. 2-D attractive potentials do not lose all their bound states as they become shallow. Solving the equivalent circular well's ground (circularly symmetric) state requires Bessel functions of the first type (J_0 inside and the modified Bessel function K_0 outside the well) but proceeds as in the above question. Only the small argument forms of these functions are required in the low energy limit.

Exercise 5.16: Consider a current $j(x)$ that varies in magnitude with position x (in 1-D); see Fig. 5.8. By calculating the *net* flow of particle probability into the interval $(x, x + \mathrm{d}x)$ show that $\partial j/\partial x = -\partial P/\partial t$. You will need the expansion Eq. (1.38). The result is a (1-D) form of Gauss's theorem and is used throughout physics. Differentiate $P = \psi^*\psi$ with respect to time, and use the time-dependent Schrödinger equation to obtain Eq. (4.21) for j.

Figure 5.8: Quantum mechanical flux j entering and leaving an interval, thereby changing the probability $P.\mathrm{d}x$ a particle can be found in it.

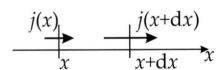

5.8 Suggestions for further reading

There are many good textbooks on quantum mechanics. We have mentioned very few sources in the text since our informal treatment is deliberately partial and incomplete. Examples of excellent and complete books on quantum mechanics at an appropriate level for continuing university level courses include (roughly in order of sophistication):

- Gillespie, *A Quantum Mechanics Primer*
  This short, but exceptionally clear, treatment of the fundamentals takes the same wavefunction approach of this text, but assumes mathematics typical of first year undergraduate studies.

- Feynman, Leighton and Sands, *The Feynman Lectures on Physics: Vol. 3*
  Feynman's classic three volume lectures are a must for any aspiring physicist. Feynman takes the matrix formulation and, with minimal mathematics, discusses a wide range of applications with his typically deep insight.

- Griffiths, *Introduction to Quantum Mechanics*
  Clear and understandable, Griffiths is a good undergraduate introduction.

- McMurray, *Quantum Mechanics*
  This is suitable for a first course in quantum mechanics and contains interactive programs to test understanding.

- Gasiorowicz, *Quantum Physics*
  Gasiorowicz's excellent text is a model exposition, taking students from the end of our text to the final undergraduate year.

- Mandl, *Quantum Mechanics*
  Mandl's solid book covers the core of an undergraduate course, anticipating misconceptions and providing hints to exercises.

- Thaller, *Visual Quantum Mechanics*
  Thaller's delightful book covers a complete introductory course on spinless particles in one and two dimensions, focusing on dynamics. The physics is brought to life by copious animations and illustrations.

We add these complementary aids to studying quantum mechanics:

- Dunningham, *Quantum Theory (Bullet Guide)*
  This miniature handbook summarises in a most compact and attractive way the essential ideas of quantum mechanics. We warmly recommend it for an overview, to know where one is going, or to find a concept quickly. Many of its ideas go beyond the scope of our text and are a good pointer to even more fascinating phenomena.

- Styer, *The Strange World of Quantum Mechanics*
  Styer's book is a qualitatively rigorous, but accessible, introduction to quantum mechanics via spin, balancing science with history. He also discusses conceptual problems and modern applications.

Index

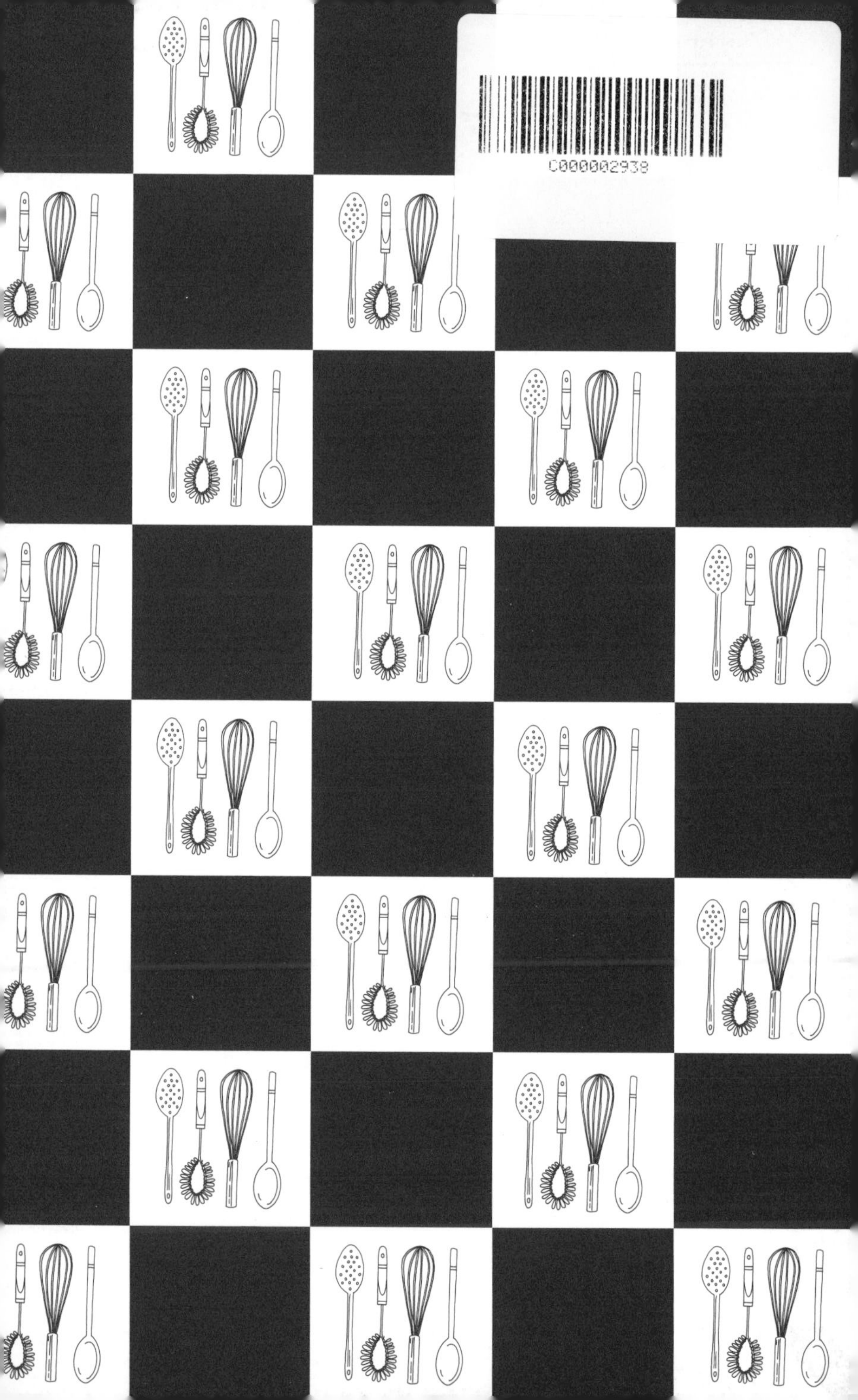

LOW-CALORIE COOKBOOK

Editor:
Valerie Ferguson

LORENZ BOOKS

Contents

Introduction

Eating a low-calorie diet that is
healthy, delicious and visually
appealing has never been easier. With
the vast range of excellent food
products available in the shops, and
our clearer understanding of the
calorific value of the various food
groups (fats, carbohydrates, etc) and
how the body uses them, it is no
longer difficult to put together truly
tasty and interesting meals that will
not pile on the pounds.

This book offers a varied selection
of recipes for soups, starters, fish,
seafood, poultry, meat and vegetarian
dishes, plus desserts with modest
calorie counts that will amaze you. Try
Cream of Grilled Pepper Soup. Enjoy
Poached Salmon with Citrus Fruits,
Skewered Lamb with Red Onion Salsa
or Rice Noodles with Vegetable Chilli
Sauce. Indulge in scrumptious
Strawberry Gâteau. You will find it
hard to believe that all of these are
low-calorie dishes.

Nutritional Notes are provided for
each recipe, giving the calorie count
per serving – soups and starters
generally average 170 calories, main
courses 210–310 calories and desserts
200 calories. Enjoy combining our
recipes as part of your calorie-
controlled diet.

Planning a Low-calorie Diet

Everyone needs the calories obtained from food as these provide the energy required to go about daily life. However, some people take in too many calories by eating too much or the wrong kind of food and may then put on excess weight.

The average daily requirement for women is 1,940 calories, and 2,550 calories for men. Most women can lose up to 4 lbs a month on a healthy diet of 1,200 – 1,500 calories (1,500–1,750 for men) a day.

How to Cut Down

The Calorie Content of Food table shows at a glance which foods are high in calories and which are not; use this as a guide. It is clear from the table that fats (such as oil and butter) and foods containing more than a little of these are the worst culprits, and foods high in carbohydrates (such as sugar) are also far from blameless. In fact, fats supply about 9 calories per gram, while carbohydrates provide about 4 calories per gram.

No matter how careful you are, you can be caught out by pre-prepared and packaged foods, such as biscuits, pastries and chocolates, which, as well as being high in sugar, can contain large amounts of "hidden" fat, which boosts their calorific value considerably. Nowadays such foods come with a breakdown of their contents, including calories, on the label and you will find that you soon become accustomed to checking this and avoiding, or at least limiting, your consumption of them.

Above: Vegetables are vital ingredients for healthy, low-calorie meals.

Keep Eating a Balanced Diet

Above: Fruit is delicious and healthy.

Current recommendations for a nutritionally balanced diet are to include a moderate amount of red meat, poultry and fish. Starchy foods (rice, pasta and bread) should provide 50 per cent of total calorie intake. At least five portions of fresh fruit and vegetables should be eaten daily. For example, one apple is a portion.

The red meats – lamb, beef and pork – are the highest in fat, and hence in calories, so it is advisable to choose chicken and turkey more often. Select lean cuts and remove the skin and any visible fat before cooking. Avoid sausages, pâtés, and pies which are usually laden with calories. Fish, particularly white fish and shellfish, are generally lower in calories than meat and are highly nutritious, so are a good choice for calorie-watchers.

Fresh vegetables and fruit, with the exception of high-fat avocados, are naturally low in calories. Nuts should be eaten in small amounts as they are high in calories. Alcohol is also high in calories and should be taken sparingly.

Cooking Methods

Whenever possible, grill, griddle, poach, steam or bake foods. If you have to fry, use as little fat as possible. Make sauces and stews by first cooking the onions and garlic in a small quantity of stock.

Labelling

Read labels carefully when choosing food. If a product claims to be low in calories, it should provide no more than 40 calories per 100 grams or 100 ml. A "reduced-calorie" product should provide no more than 75 per cent of the calories found in the standard product..

The Calorie Content of Food

This chart shows the energy content (measured in calories) of 25 g/1 oz of different foods.

Energy

Breads, cereals, biscuits & preserves	
Bread, white	59 Kcals/251 kJ
Bread, wholemeal (whole-wheat)	54 Kcals/228 kJ
Rice, white, uncooked	90 Kcals/384 kJ
Pasta, white, uncooked	86 Kcals/364 kJ
Cake, fruit, plain, store-bought	89 Kcals/372 kJ
Jam	65 Kcals/273 kJ
Chocolate, plain	127 Kcals/534 kJ

Eggs & oils	
Egg, boiled (half an egg)	37 Kcals/153 kJ
Egg, white	9 Kcals/38 kJ
Egg, yolk	85 Kcals/351 kJ
Oil, sunflower	225 Kcals/924 kJ
Oil, olive	225 Kcals/924 kJ

Poultry, meat & meat products	
Chicken, roast, meat & skin	54 Kcals/226 kJ
Chicken, roast, meat only	37 Kcals/155 kJ
Turkey, roast, meat & skin	43 Kcals/179 kJ
Turkey, roast, meat only	35 Kcals/148 kJ
Bacon, back, grilled, fat trimmed	53 Kcals/223 kJ
Beef, roast, topside, lean	39 Kcals/165 kJ
Lamb, loin chop, grilled, lean	62 Kcals/260 kJ
Lamb, leg, roast, lean	53 Kcals/220 kJ
Pork, loin chop, grilled, lean	46 Kcals/193 kJ
Liver pâté	87 Kcals/359 kJ
Pork pie, individual	94 Kcals/391 kJ

Fish	
Cod, raw	20 Kcals/84 kJ
Cod, fried in batter	61 Kcals/255 kJ
Prawns (shrimp), cooked, no shell	25 Kcals/105 kJ
Salmon, canned	38 Kcals/161 kJ
Salmon, grilled	54 Kcals/224 kJ
Trout, grilled	34 Kcals/141 kJ
Tuna, raw	34 Kcals/141 kJ
Tuna, canned in brine	25 Kcals/106 kJ

Vegetables	
Broccoli, boiled	6 Kcals/25 kJ
Brussels sprouts, boiled	9 Kcals/37 kJ
Cauliflower, boiled	7 Kcals/29 kJ
Celery, raw	2 Kcals/8 kJ
Courgettes (zucchini), boiled	5 Kcals/20 kJ
Mushrooms, raw	3 Kcals/12 kJ
Leeks, boiled	5 Kcals/22 kJ
Peas, boiled	17 Kcals/73 kJ
Peppers, raw	4 Kcals/16 kJ
Potatoes, new, boiled	19 Kcals/78 kJ
Chips (French fries), oven baked	39 Kcals/166 kJ
Chips, fried, retail	59 Kcals/246 kJ
Tomatoes, raw	4 Kcals/18 kJ

Fruit & nuts	
Apple	11 Kcals/45 kJ
Avocado	48 Kcals/196 kJ
Banana	24 Kcals/101 kJ
Dried mixed fruit	67 Kcals/281 kJ
Orange	9 Kcals/39 kJ
Peach	8 Kcals/35 kJ
Strawberries	7 Kcals/28 kJ
Almonds	153 Kcals/633 kJ
Cashews, roasted	153 Kcals/633 kJ
Coconut, desiccated	151 Kcals/623 kJ
Peanuts, roasted	150 Kcals/623 kJ
Sesame seeds	148 Kcals/618 kJ

Dairy produce	
Cream, double (heavy)	112 Kcals/462 kJ
Cream, single (light)	49 Kcals/204 kJ
Milk, whole	16 Kcals/69 kJ
Milk, semi-skimmed (low-fat)	11 Kcals/49 kJ
Milk, skimmed (skim)	8 Kcals/35 kJ
Margarine	185 Kcals/760 kJ
Butter	184 Kcals/758 kJ
Low-fat spread (40%)	98 Kcals/401 kJ
Very low-fat spread (25%)	68 Kcals/282 kJ
Crème fraîche	78 Kcals/324 kJ
Crème fraîche, low fat	42 Kcals/173 kJ
Fromage frais	28 Kcals/117 kJ
Fromage frais, very low fat	15 Kcals/62 kJ
Cheese, Cheddar	103 Kcals/427 kJ
Cheese, Cheddar, reduced fat	65 Kcals/273 kJ
Cheese, Edam	83 Kcals/346 kJ
Yogurt, plain, low fat	13 Kcals/54 kJ
Greek yogurt (plain, strained)	29 Kcals/119 kJ

Low-calorie Ingredients & Substitutes

To help with your calorie-controlled diet, look out for the many lower fat and lower sugar or "diet" versions of standard foods now available.

Dairy Produce

Milk Choose semi-skimmed (low-fat) (1.5–1.8 per cent fat) or skimmed (skim) (0.3 per cent fat) milk.

Yogurt Low-fat (about 1 per cent fat) and "diet" (0.3 per cent fat) natural yogurts are an excellent substitute for cream.

Crème fraîche Delicious served with desserts and successful in cooking, the half-fat version contains about 15 per cent fat.

Fromage frais A fresh-tasting soft cheese, available as virtually fat-free (0.4 per cent fat). Useful as an accompaniment for desserts and for filling and topping cakes.

Cottage cheese A low-fat soft cheese, which is also available in a half-fat version.

Half fat hard cheese Several kinds of hard cheese are now obtainable in half-fat form, including Cheddar and Red Leicester (both about 14 per cent fat).

Spreads

For spreading on bread, try reduced-fat butter or a low-fat spread made with a high proportion of buttermilk or with sunflower or olive oil, all of which contain about 40 per cent fat. There are also very low-fat spreads

Above: Low-fat yogurt and cheeses are widely available in supermarkets.

that contain 20–30 per cent fat. None of these reduced-fat spreads is suitable for baking.

Sweeteners

Sugar and honey As these are both high in calories, they should be used sparingly. Dark sugar and honey have more flavour so you can usually get away with using less.

Artificial sweeteners Available in liquid, granulated and "tablet" form, these are a useful alternative to sugar for sweetening recipes and drinks. Most contain about one-tenth the calories of sugar.

Fruit spreads and juices Use concentrated, unsweetened fruit spreads and juices sparingly as sweeteners for all kinds of desserts.

Tomato & Basil-flower Soup

A pretty, fresh-tasting chilled soup with a low calorie count.

Serves 4

INGREDIENTS
1 onion, chopped
1 garlic clove, crushed
15 ml/1 tbsp olive oil
600 ml/1 pint/2½ cups vegetable stock
900 g/2 lb tomatoes, roughly chopped
20 basil leaves, plus extra to garnish
few drops of elderflower or balsamic vinegar
juice of ½ lemon
150 ml/¼ pint/⅔ cup plain low-fat yogurt
sugar and salt, to taste
30 ml/2 tbsp plain low-fat yogurt and
    10 ml/2 tsp basil flowers, to garnish

1 Fry the onion and garlic in the oil
for 2–3 minutes until soft. Add 300 ml/
½ pint/1¼ cups of the stock and the
tomatoes. Bring to the boil, lower the
heat and simmer for 15 minutes.

2 Allow to cool slightly, then process
in a blender or food processor. Strain.
Add the remaining stock, half the basil
leaves, the vinegar, lemon juice and
yogurt to the puréed tomatoes. Season
with sugar and salt to taste. Process
until smooth. Chill.

3 Just before serving, finely shred the
remaining basil leaves and add to the
soup. Pour into individual bowls.
Garnish with yogurt topped with a
few small basil leaves and flowers
and serve.

Nutritional Notes	
Energy	97 Kcals/403 kJ
Fat, total	3.8 g
Saturated fat	0.8 g
Cholesterol	1.5 mg

Spicy Tomato & Lentil Soup

This warming soup is flavoured with a hint of fresh ginger and cumin.

Serves 4

INGREDIENTS
15 ml/1 tbsp sunflower oil
1 onion, finely chopped
1–2 garlic cloves, crushed
2.5 cm/1 in piece fresh root ginger, peeled
　and finely chopped
5 ml/1 tsp cumin seed, crushed
450 g/1 lb ripe tomatoes, peeled, seeded and
　chopped
115 g/4 oz/½ cup split red lentils
1.2 litres/2 pints/5 cups vegetable or chicken
　stock
15 ml/1 tbsp tomato purée (paste)
salt and freshly ground black pepper
low-fat plain yogurt and chopped fresh
　parsley, to garnish (optional)

1 Heat the oil and cook the onion gently for about 5 minutes until softened. Add the garlic, ginger, cumin, tomatoes and lentils. Cook over a low heat for a further 3–4 minutes.

2 Stir in the stock and tomato purée. Bring to the boil, and simmer gently for about 30 minutes until the lentils are soft. Season to taste.

3 Purée the soup in a blender or food processor. Reheat, then serve garnished with a little yogurt and parsley, if liked.

Nutritional Notes	
Energy	151 Kcals/628 kJ
Fat, total	3.5 g
Saturated fat	0.5 g
Cholesterol	0 mg

Cream of Grilled Pepper Soup

This is a creamy but light, nutritious and colourful soup.

Serves 4

INGREDIENTS

3 large red (bell) peppers, halved and seeded
1 large yellow (bell) pepper, halved and
    seeded
15 ml/1 tbsp olive oil
1 small shallot, chopped
600 ml/1 pint/2½ cups vegetable stock
2 garlic cloves, crushed
1.5 ml/¼ tsp saffron strands
150 ml/¼ pint/⅔ cup single (light) cream
475 ml/16 fl oz/2 cups water
salt and freshly ground black pepper
fresh chervil or flat leaf parsley sprigs, to
    garnish and Melba toast, to serve

1 Grill (broil) the peppers until
blackened then place them in a plastic
bag and leave to cool. Peel, then reserve
one quarter each of a red and yellow
pepper and roughly chop the remainder.

2 Heat the oil and sauté the shallot
until soft. Add the stock, garlic, saffron
and chopped peppers. Bring to the boil
and simmer for 15 minutes. Cool for
10 minutes, then process in a blender
or food processor until smooth.

3 Return the soup to a clean pan.
Mix together the cream and water and
add to the soup with seasoning.
Reheat gently. Pour the soup into
bowls and garnish with thin strips of
the reserved peppers and herb sprigs.
Serve with Melba toast.

Nutritional Notes	
Energy	153 Kcals/636 kJ
Fat, total	10.5 g
Saturated fat	4.9 g
Cholesterol	20.6 mg

Farmhouse Soup

Root vegetables form the base of this chunky, minestrone-style soup.

Serves 4

INGREDIENTS
15 ml/1 tbsp olive oil
1 onion, roughly chopped
2 carrots, cut into chunks
150–175 g/5–6 oz turnips, cut into chunks
about 150 g/5 oz swede, cut into chunks
400 g/14 oz can chopped tomatoes
15 ml/1 tbsp tomato purée (paste)
5 ml/1 tsp dried mixed herbs
5 ml/1 tsp dried oregano
50 g/2 oz/½ cup dried (bell) peppers, washed
  and thinly sliced (optional)
1.5 litres/2½ pints/6¼ cups vegetable stock
  or water
50 g/2 oz/½ cup dried small macaroni
200 g/7 oz canned red kidney beans, rinsed
  and drained
30 ml/2 tbsp chopped fresh flat leaf parsley
salt and freshly ground black pepper
grated Parmesan cheese, to serve (optional)

1 Heat the oil and cook the onion for 5 minutes until softened. Add the next eight ingredients. Season to taste. Add the stock or water and bring to the boil. Cover and simmer for 30 minutes, stirring occasionally.

2 Add the pasta and bring to the boil, stirring. Simmer, uncovered, until the pasta is *al dente*.

3 Stir in the beans. Heat through for 2–3 minutes, then remove from the heat and add the parsley. Serve with grated Parmesan handed separately, if liked.

Nutritional Notes	
Energy	182 Kcals/756 kJ
Fat, total	3.8 g
Saturated fat	0.5 g
Cholesterol	0 mg

Chicken & Mushroom Terrine

Proof that a terrine can be mouthwatering without being calorie-loaded.

Serves 4

INGREDIENTS

2 shallots, chopped
175 g/6 oz/2 cups mushrooms, chopped
45 ml/3 tbsp chicken stock
2 skinless chicken breasts, chopped
1 egg white
30 ml/2 tbsp wholewheat breadcrumbs
30 ml/2 tbsp chopped fresh parsley
30 ml/2 tbsp chopped fresh sage
salt and freshly ground black pepper

1 Preheat the oven to 180°C/350°F/
Gas 4. Place the shallots, mushrooms
and stock in a pan and cook gently,
stirring occasionally, until the
vegetables have softened and the stock
has evaporated.

2 Place in a food processor with the
chopped chicken breasts, egg white,
breadcrumbs and seasoning and chop
coarsely. Add the herbs. Spoon into a
greased 900 ml/1½ pint/3¾ cup loaf
tin and smooth the surface.

3 Cover the tin with foil and bake for
35–40 minutes until the juices are no
longer pink. Place a weight on top,
leave to cool, then chill. Serve the
terrine sliced.

Nutritional Notes	
Energy	140 Kcals/582 kJ
Fat, total	2.9 g
Saturated fat	0.7 g
Cholesterol	61.0 mg

Guacamole with Crudités

This spicy dip is made using peas instead of the traditional avocados.

Serves 4–6

INGREDIENTS

350 g/12 oz/3 cups frozen peas, defrosted
1 garlic clove, crushed
2 spring onions(scallions), chopped
5 ml/1 tsp finely grated rind and juice of 1
    lime
2.5 ml/½ tsp ground cumin
dash of Tabasco sauce
15 ml/1 tbsp reduced-calorie mayonnaise
30 ml/2 tbsp chopped fresh coriander (cilantro)
1 dessert apple, cored and sliced
1 pear, peeled, cored and sliced
15 ml/1 tbsp lemon or lime juice
6 baby carrots
2 celery sticks, halved lengthways and cut
    into sticks
6 baby sweetcorn (baby corn)
salt and freshly ground black pepper
pinch of paprika and lime slices, to garnish

1 Put the first seven ingredients and seasoning into a food processor or a blender and process until smooth.

2 Add the coriander and process for a few more seconds. Spoon into a serving bowl, cover and chill for 30 minutes, to let the flavours develop.

3 Dip the apple and pear slices into the lemon or lime juice. Arrange with the carrots, celery and baby sweetcorn on a platter. Sprinkle the paprika over the guacamole, garnish with lime and serve with the crudités.

Nutritional Notes	
Energy	110 Kcals/460 kJ
Fat, total	2.29 g
Saturated fat	0.49 g
Cholesterol	30.0 mg

Vegetables Provençale

The flavours of the Mediterranean are created in this delicious vegetable dish, which makes an ideal low-calorie starter.

Serves 6

INGREDIENTS

1 onion, sliced
2 leeks, sliced
2 garlic cloves, crushed
1 red (bell) pepper, seeded and sliced
1 green (bell) pepper, seeded and sliced
1 yellow (bell) pepper, seeded and sliced
350 g/12 oz/2½ cups courgettes (zucchini), sliced
225 g/8 oz/3 cups mushrooms, sliced
400 g/14 oz can chopped tomatoes
30 ml/2 tbsp ruby port
30 ml/2 tbsp tomato purée (paste)
15 ml/1 tbsp tomato ketchup
400 g/14 oz can chickpeas
115 g/4 oz/1 cup pitted black olives
45 ml/3 tbsp chopped fresh mixed herbs, plus extra to garnish

2 Drain the chickpeas, rinse in cold water, drain again, then add to the pan. Stir well.

3 Cover, bring to the boil and simmer gently for 20–30 minutes until the vegetables are tender but not overcooked, stirring occasionally.

1 Put the onion, leeks, garlic, peppers, courgettes and mushrooms into a large pan. Add the tomatoes, port, tomato purée and tomato ketchup and mix thoroughly.

Nutritional Notes	
Energy	155 Kcals/654 kJ
Fat, total	4.56 g
Saturated fat	0.67 g
Cholesterol	0 mg

4 Remove the lid from the pan and increase the heat slightly for the last 10 minutes of the cooking time to thicken the sauce if liked.

5 Stir in the olives, chopped herbs and season with salt and pepper to taste. Serve hot or cold, garnished with chopped mixed herbs.

Monkfish Kebabs with Lemon & Thyme

These delicate, fresh flavourings are a perfect complement to monkfish.

Serves 4

INGREDIENTS
675 g/1½ lb monkfish fillet
15 ml/1 tbsp olive oil
1 garlic clove, crushed
finely grated rind and juice of 1 lemon
30 ml/2 tbsp chopped fresh thyme
8 lemon wedges
salt and freshly ground black pepper
green salad and crusty bread, to serve

1 Cut the fish into even-size pieces and place in a bowl. Add the oil, garlic, lemon rind and juice, thyme, and seasoning, then stir well to coat the fish evenly.

2 Preheat the grill (broiler) or prepare a barbecue. Thread the fish pieces on to four metal skewers and secure with lemon wedges at each end.

3 Cook the kebabs under the grill, or on the barbecue, for 7–8 minutes or until just cooked through, turning once. Serve with salad and bread.

Nutritional Notes	
Energy	136 Kcals/565 kJ
Fat, total	3.4 g
Saturated fat	0.5 g
Cholesterol	23.6 mg

Italian Fish Stew

A richly flavoured main course dish that is surprisingly low in calories.

Serves 4

INGREDIENTS

10 ml/2 tsp olive oil
1 medium red onion, finely chopped
1 garlic clove, crushed
1 small fennel bulb, sliced
400 g/14 oz can chopped tomatoes
10 ml/2 tsp fennel seeds
175 ml/6 fl oz/¾ cup fish stock
450 g/1 lb cod or haddock fillet, cut into
    chunks
15 g/½ oz/4 tbsp chopped fresh basil
4 lemon slices
salt and freshly ground black pepper

1 Heat the olive oil in a large pan and fry the onion, garlic and sliced fennel gently until they are softened but not browned.

2 Add the tomatoes, fennel seeds and fish stock and bring to the boil. Add the diced fish, basil, lemon slices, salt and pepper.

3 Cover and simmer very gently for 6–8 minutes until the fish is just cooked through. Serve hot.

VARIATION: Almost any type of white fish can be used in place of the cod or haddock.

Nutritional Notes	
Energy	127 Kcals/528 kJ
Fat, total	2.6 g
Saturated fat	0.4 g
Cholesterol	43.8 mg

Whole Sea Bass *en Papillote*

This way of cooking a whole fish enclosed in a paper parcel keeps it moist and retains the maximum flavour.

Serves 4

INGREDIENTS

1.5 kg/3–3½ lb fresh whole sea bass, cleaned, scaled and head removed
5 fresh mint sprigs
½ lemon, sliced
2 shallots, finely sliced
2 fresh plum tomatoes, sliced
15 ml/1 tbsp olive oil
salt and freshly ground black pepper
steamed broccoli, to serve

2 Season the fish inside and out with salt and pepper.

3 Tuck the fresh mint sprigs and lemon, shallots and tomato slices inside the fish and drizzle the olive oil over its back.

1 Preheat the oven to 180°C/350°F/ Gas 4. Wash and dry the sea bass and place on a double piece of nonstick baking parchment large enough to wrap the fish comfortably and loosely.

4 Fold the paper over the fish and double fold the three open edges for a tight seal. Place the fish on a baking sheet and bake for 40–50 minutes until cooked through.

5 Cut the package open with scissors and serve the fish immediately, accompanied by steamed broccoli.

Nutritional Notes	
Energy	301 Kcals/1252 kJ
Fat, total	15.3 g
Saturated fat	7.63 g
Cholesterol	163 mg

COOK'S TIP: Sea bass is also known as sea wolf, sea perch or sea dace and has delicate pink flesh and a light, sweet smell. Large fish are ideal for stuffing, as here, and small fish can be grilled or barbecued.

Monkfish & Scallop Skewers

Lemon grass imbues the seafood with a subtle citrus taste.

Serves 4

INGREDIENTS
8 lemon grass stalks
30 ml/2 tbsp lemon juice
15 ml/1 tbsp olive oil
15 ml/1 tbsp finely chopped fresh coriander
   (cilantro)
2.5 ml/½ tsp salt
large pinch of ground black pepper
450 g/1 lb monkfish fillet, cut into 16 chunks
12 large scallops, halved crossways
fresh coriander leaves, to garnish
rice, to serve

1 Remove the outer leaves from the lemon grass. Chop the tender parts of the lemon grass leaves finely and place in a bowl. Stir in the lemon juice, oil, chopped coriander, salt and pepper.

2 Thread the fish chunks and scallop halves alternately on the eight lemon grass stalks. Arrange the skewers of fish and shellfish in a shallow dish and pour over the lemon mixture.

3 Cover and leave to marinate for 1 hour, turning occasionally. Transfer the skewers to a heatproof dish or bamboo steamer, cover and steam over boiling water for 10 minutes until just cooked. Garnish with coriander and serve with rice and the cooking juice poured over.

Nutritional Notes	
Energy	158 Kcals/657 kJ
Fat, total	3.9 g
Saturated fat	0.7 g
Cholesterol	39.2 mg

Caribbean Fish Steaks

Serves 4

INGREDIENTS
15 ml/1 tbsp oil
6 shallots, finely chopped
1 garlic clove, crushed
1 fresh green chilli, seeded and finely
  chopped
400 g/14 oz can chopped tomatoes
2 bay leaves
1.5 ml/¼ tsp cayenne pepper
5 ml/1 tsp crushed allspice
juice of 2 limes
4 cod steaks
5 ml/1 tsp brown muscovado (brown) sugar
10 ml/2 tsp angostura bitters
salt
steamed okra or green beans, to serve

1 Heat the oil in a frying pan. Add
the shallots and cook for 5 minutes
until soft.

2 Add the garlic and chilli and cook
for 2 minutes, then stir in the tomatoes,
bay leaves, cayenne pepper, allspice and
lime juice, with a little salt to taste.

3 Cook gently for 15 minutes, then
add the cod steaks and baste with the
tomato sauce. Cover and cook for 10
minutes or until the steaks are just
cooked through. Remove and keep hot.

4 Stir the sugar and angostura bitters
into the sauce, simmer for 2 minutes,
then pour over the fish. Serve with
steamed okra or green beans.

Nutritional Notes	
Energy	190 Kcals/790 kJ
Fat, total	4 g
Saturated fat	0.6 g
Cholesterol	58.5 mg

Cod, Tomato & Pepper Bake

This appetizing, potato-topped bake is filling and substantial yet relatively low in calories. It needs only a salad or lightly cooked vegetable accompaniment to make a satisfying meal.

Serves 4

INGREDIENTS
450 g/1 lb potatoes, thinly sliced
15 ml/1 tbsp olive oil
1 red onion, chopped
1 garlic clove, crushed
1 red (bell) pepper, seeded and diced
1 yellow (bell) pepper, seeded and diced
225 g/8 oz/3 cups mushrooms, sliced
400 g/14 oz and 225 g/8 oz cans chopped
   tomatoes
75 ml/5 tbsp fish or vegetable stock
75 ml/5 tbsp dry white wine
450 g/1 lb skinless, boneless cod fillet, cut
   into 2 cm/³⁄₄ in cubes
50 g/2 oz/½ cup pitted black olives, chopped
15 ml/1 tbsp chopped fresh basil
15 ml/1 tbsp chopped fresh oregano
salt and freshly ground black pepper
fresh oregano sprigs, to garnish
steamed courgettes (zucchini), to serve

1 Preheat the oven to 200°C/400°F/ Gas 6. Par-boil the potatoes in a pan of lightly salted, boiling water for 4 minutes. Drain thoroughly. Set aside.

2 Heat the remaining oil in a pan, add the onion, garlic and diced red and yellow peppers and cook for 5 minutes, stirring occasionally.

3 Stir in the sliced mushrooms, chopped tomatoes, stock and wine, bring to the boil and boil rapidly for a few minutes until the sauce has reduced slightly.

4 Add the fish cubes and chopped olives, basil and oregano to the tomato mixture. Season to taste with salt and ground black pepper.

5 Spoon into a lightly greased ovenproof dish and arrange the potato slices over the top, covering the fish mixture completely.

6 Bake, uncovered, for about 45 minutes until the fish is cooked and tender and the potato topping is lightly browned. Garnish with fresh oregano sprigs and serve with steamed courgettes.

Nutritional Notes	
Energy	280 Kcals/1165 kJ
Fat, total	5.9 g
Saturated fat	0.8 g
Cholesterol	51.8 mg

Poached Salmon with Citrus Fruits

An elegant, but simple, dish with delightfully contrasting flavours.

Serves 4

INGREDIENTS
2 shallots, finely chopped
300 ml/½ pint/1¼ cups fish stock
4 salmon cutlets, about 150 g/5 oz each
1 lime
1 medium orange
1 small pink grapefruit
salt and freshly ground black pepper
steamed new potatoes, to serve (optional)

1 Place the finely chopped shallots in a wide pan with the fish stock. Simmer gently for 6–8 minutes until the stock has reduced by half and the shallots are transparent.

2 Arrange the cutlets in a single layer on the shallots, cover and simmer for 5 minutes until the fish is just cooked.

3 Remove a few strips of citrus rind and set aside. Peel and segment the fruits, collecting the juices. Add to the pan, heat and season. Garnish with rind strips and serve with potatoes, if using.

Nutritional Notes	
Energy	291 Kcals/1210 kJ
Fat, total	16.2 g
Saturated fat	3.2 g
Cholesterol	73.5 mg

Spicy Prawns with Campanelle

Serves 6

INGREDIENTS
225 g/8 oz cooked peeled tiger prawns
  (shrimp)
150 g/5 oz smoked turkey rashers (bacon)
1 shallot or small onion, finely chopped
60 ml/4 tbsp white wine
225 g/8 oz/3 cups campanelle
60 ml/4 tbsp fish stock
4 ripe tomatoes, peeled, seeded and chopped
10 g/¼ oz/2 tbsp chopped fresh parsley
salt and freshly ground black pepper

FOR THE MARINADE
1–2 garlic cloves, crushed
finely grated rind of 1 lemon
15 ml/1 tbsp lemon juice
1.5 ml/¼ tsp red chilli paste
15 ml/1 tbsp light soy sauce

1 Marinate the prawns with the marinade ingredients and seasoning for at least 1 hour.

2 Grill the turkey rashers, then cut them into 5 mm/¼ in dice.

3 Put the chopped shallot or onion and white wine into a pan, bring to the boil, cover and cook for 2–3 minutes or until the wine has reduced by half. Cook the campanelle in boiling, salted water according to the packet instructions until *al dente*. Drain thoroughly.

4 Put the prawns and marinade in a large frying pan, bring to the boil and add the turkey and stock. Heat for 1 minute, then add to the pasta with the tomatoes and parsley, toss and serve.

Nutritional Notes	
Energy	203 Kcals/844 kJ
Fat, total	1.3 g
Saturated fat	0.3 g
Cholesterol	87 mg

Chicken Baked with Butter Beans & Garlic

A whole bird is cooked slowly on a bed of garlicky vegetables.

Serves 6

INGREDIENTS

2 leeks, thickly sliced
1 small fennel bulb, roughly chopped
4 garlic cloves, peeled
2 x 400 g/14 oz cans butter (lima) beans,
   drained and rinsed
2 large handfuls fresh parsley, chopped, with
   a few sprigs reserved to garnish
300 ml/½ pint/1¼ cups dry white wine
300 ml/½ pint/1¼ cups vegetable stock
1.5 kg/3½ lb chicken
cooked green vegetables, to serve

1 Preheat the oven to
180°C/350°F/Gas 4. Mix the leeks,
fennel, whole garlic cloves, beans and
chopped parsley in a bowl.

2 Spread out the mixture on the
bottom of a heavy-based, flameproof
casserole large enough to hold the
chicken. Pour in the wine and stock.

3 Place the chicken on top. Bring to
the boil, cover the casserole and
transfer it to the oven. Bake for 1–1½
hours until the chicken is cooked and
so tender that it falls off the bone.
Garnish with parsley sprigs and serve
with lightly cooked green vegetables.

Nutritional Notes	
Energy	304 Kcals/1288 kJ
Fat, total	3.4 g
Saturated fat	0.8 g
Cholesterol	114 mg

Poached Chicken with Mustard Mayonnaise

This method of cooking keeps chicken succulent and tasty.

Serves 4

INGREDIENTS
1 leek, roughly chopped
1 large carrot, roughly chopped
1 celery stick, roughly chopped
1 medium onion, roughly chopped
1.5 kg/3½ lb chicken
15 ml/1 tbsp roughly chopped fresh parsley
10 ml/2 tsp roughly chopped fresh thyme
6 fresh green peppercorns
60 ml/4 tbsp mustard mayonnaise (made by mixing reduced-calorie mayonnaise with Dijon mustard to taste), green salad and lightly cooked baby carrots, to serve

1 Place the leek, carrot, celery and onion in a large pan.

2 Place the chicken on top, cover with water and bring to the boil. Remove any scum that comes to the surface. Add the herbs and peppercorns. Simmer gently for 1 hour. Remove from the heat and cool in the broth.

3 Transfer the chicken to a board or plate and carve, removing the skin. Arrange the slices on a serving platter. Serve with mustard mayonnaise, green salad and lightly cooked baby carrots.

Nutritional Notes	
Energy	153 Kcals/636 kJ
Fat, total	5 g
Saturated fat	1.4 g
Cholesterol	85 mg

Chicken with Mixed Vegetables

A stir-fry with an oriental flavour, this uses very little oil and so makes a great low-calorie main course dish.

Serves 4

INGREDIENTS
350 g/12 oz skinless chicken breast fillets
20 ml/4 tsp vegetable oil
300 ml/½ pint/1¼ cups chicken stock
75 g/3 oz/¾ cup drained, canned
    straw mushrooms
50 g/2 oz/½ cup drained, canned sliced
    bamboo shoots
50 g/2 oz/⅓ cup drained, canned water
    chestnuts, sliced
1 small carrot, sliced
50 g/2 oz/½ cup mangetouts (snowpeas)
15 ml/1 tbsp dry sherry
15 ml/1 tbsp oyster sauce
5 ml/1 tsp caster sugar
5 ml/1 tsp cornflour (cornstarch)
15 ml/1 tbsp cold water
salt and freshly ground black pepper

1 Put the chicken in a shallow bowl. Add 5 ml/1 tsp of the oil, 1.5 ml/ ¼ tsp salt and a pinch of pepper. Cover and set the chicken aside for 10 minutes in a cool place.

Nutritional Notes	
Energy	148 Kcals/615 kJ
Fat, total	5.6 g
Saturated fat	1 g
Cholesterol	61 mg

2 Bring the stock to the boil in a saucepan. Add the chicken and cook for 12 minutes or until tender. Drain and slice thickly, reserving 75 ml/ 5 tbsp of the stock.

3 Heat the remaining oil in a non-stick frying pan or wok, add all the vegetables and stir-fry for 2 minutes. Stir in the sherry, oyster sauce, caster sugar and reserved stock. Add the chicken to the pan and cook for 2 minutes more.

4 Mix the cornflour to a paste with the water. Add the mixture to the pan and cook, stirring, until the sauce thickens slightly. Season to taste with salt and pepper and serve immediately.

VARIATION: Try courgettes, broccoli and beansprouts, if you like.

31

Turkey Picadillo

Using minced turkey rather than beef for this Mexican-style dish makes it much lower in calories.

Serves 4

INGREDIENTS
15 ml/1 tbsp sunflower oil
1 onion, chopped
250 g/9 oz minced (ground) turkey
1–2 garlic cloves, crushed
1 fresh green chilli, seeded and finely
    chopped
6 tomatoes, peeled and chopped
15 ml/1 tbsp tomato purée (paste) or sun-
    dried tomato purée (paste)
2.5 ml/½ tsp ground cumin
1 yellow or orange (bell) pepper, chopped
25 g/1 oz/⅙ cup raisins
25 g/1 oz/¼ cup flaked almonds, toasted
    (optional)
45 ml/3 tbsp chopped fresh coriander
    (cilantro)
150 ml/¼ pint/⅔ cup plain low-fat yogurt
2–3 spring onions (scallions), finely chopped
4 small soft tortillas
salt and freshly ground black pepper
shredded lettuce, to serve

1 Heat the oil in a large frying pan and add the onion. Cook gently until soft. Stir in the minced turkey and garlic and cook gently for 5 minutes.

VARIATION: Turkey Picadillo and the topping can also be used with baked jacket potatoes; adjust your calorie count accordingly.

2 Stir in the green chilli, chopped tomatoes, tomato purée, cumin, yellow or orange pepper and raisins. Cover and cook over a gentle heat for 15 minutes, stirring occasionally and adding a little water if necessary.

3 Stir in the toasted almonds, if using, with about two-thirds of the coriander. Add salt and pepper to taste.

4 Tip the low-fat yogurt into a bowl. Stir in the remaining coriander and the chopped spring onions. Heat the tortillas in a dry frying pan, without oil, for 15–20 seconds.

5 Place some shredded lettuce and turkey mixture on each tortilla, roll up like a pancake and transfer to a plate. Top with a generous spoonful of the yogurt and coriander mixture and serve immediately.

Nutritional Notes	
Energy	295 Kcals/1225 kJ
Fat, total	8.6 g
Saturated fat	0.9 g
Cholesterol	45.3 mg

Chinese Pork

It is worth allowing plenty of time for marinating this lean pork fillet, which is then roasted to produce a truly mouthwatering result. Steamed vegetables would complement the richness of the pork perfectly.

Serves 6

INGREDIENTS
900 g/2 lb pork fillet, trimmed
15 ml/1 tbsp clear honey
45 ml/3 tbsp rice wine or medium-dry sherry
spring onion (scallion) curls, to garnish

FOR THE MARINADE
150 ml/¼ pint/⅔ cup dark soy sauce
90 ml/6 tbsp rice wine or medium-dry sherry
150 ml/¼ pint/⅔ cup well-flavoured chicken
   stock
15 ml/1 tbsp soft brown sugar
1 cm/½ in piece fresh root ginger, peeled and
   finely sliced
40 ml/2½ tbsp chopped onion

2 Put the pork fillet in a shallow dish that is large enough to hold it in a single layer. Pour over 250 ml/8 fl oz/1 cup of the marinade, cover and chill for at least 8 hours, turning the meat several times.

1 To make the marinade, place all the ingredients in a pan and stir over a medium heat until the mixture boils. Lower the heat and simmer gently for 15 minutes, stirring from time to time. Leave to cool.

3 Preheat the oven to 200°C/400°F/Gas 6. Drain the pork, reserving the marinade in the dish. Place the meat on a rack over a roasting tin and pour water into the tin to a depth of 1 cm/½ in. Place the tin in the oven and roast for 20 minutes.

Nutritional Notes	
Energy	206 Kcals/856 kJ
Fat, total	6 g
Saturated fat	2.1 g
Cholesterol	94.5 mg

4 Stir the honey and rice wine or sherry into the marinade. Remove the meat from the oven and place in the marinade, turning to coat.

5 Put the meat back on the rack and roast for 20–30 minutes more or until cooked. Serve hot or cold, in slices, garnished with spring onion curls

COOK'S TIP: To make spring onion curls, cut spring onions down to 7.5 cm/3 in lengths, then cut lengthways, leaving the root end intact. Place in iced water and chill until curled.

35

Skewered Lamb with Red Onion Salsa

A low-calorie dish that is bursting with taste sensations, both from the spicy marinade coating the lamb and the fresh vegetables and herbs of the salsa.

Serves 2

INGREDIENTS
225 g/8 oz lean lamb, cubed
2.5 ml/½ tsp ground cumin
5 ml/1 tsp ground paprika
15 ml/1 tbsp olive oil
salt and freshly ground black pepper

FOR THE SALSA
1 red onion, very thinly sliced
1 large tomato, seeded and chopped
15 ml/1 tbsp red wine vinegar
3–4 fresh basil or mint leaves, roughly torn
small mint leaves, to garnish

1 Place the lamb in a bowl with the cumin, paprika, oil and plenty of salt and pepper. Toss well until the lamb is coated with spices.

2 Cover the bowl with clear film (plastic wrap) and leave in a cool place for several hours, or in the fridge overnight, to marinade the lamb.

VARIATION: For an alternative to the red onion salsa, stir chopped fresh mint or basil and a little lemon juice into a small pot of low-fat Greek-style yogurt. Adjust your calorie count accordingly.

3 Spear the lamb cubes on to four small skewers – if using wooden skewers, soak them first in cold water for at least 30 minutes to prevent them burning under the grill (broiler).

4 To make the salsa, put the onion, tomato, vinegar and basil or mint leaves in a small bowl and stir together until thoroughly blended. Season to taste with salt, garnish with mint, then set aside while you cook the lamb.

5 Cook the lamb over hot coals or under a preheated grill for about 5–10 minutes, turning the skewers frequently, until the lamb is well browned but still slightly pink in the centre. Serve hot, with the salsa.

Nutritional Notes	
Energy	132 Kcals/549 kJ
Fat, total	7.6 g
Saturated fat	2.5 g
Cholesterol	41.6 mg

Beef Strips with Orange & Ginger

This delicious, lean beef dish is quickly prepared by stir-frying, one of the best methods of low-calorie cooking.

Serves 4

INGREDIENTS
450 g/1 lb lean beef rump, fillet or sirloin,
    cut into thin strips
finely grated rind and juice of 1 orange
15 ml/1 tbsp light soy sauce
5 ml/1 tsp cornflour (cornstarch)
2.5 cm/1 in piece fresh root ginger, peeled
    and finely chopped
10 ml/2 tsp sesame oil
1 large carrot, cut into thin strips
2 spring onions (scallions), thinly sliced
cooked rice noodles, to serve

3 Heat the oil in a wok or large frying pan and add the beef. Stir-fry for 1 minute until lightly coloured, then add the carrot and stir-fry for a further 2–3 minutes.

1 Place the beef strips in a bowl and sprinkle over the orange rind and juice. If possible, leave to marinate for at least 30 minutes.

2 Drain the liquid from the meat and set aside, then mix the marinade with the soy sauce, cornflour and ginger.

4 Stir in the spring onions and reserved liquid, then cook, stirring, until boiling and thickened. Serve hot with rice noodles.

VARIATION: Lean pork tenderloin or fillet could be used instead of beef. Adjust your calorie count accordingly.

Nutritional Notes	
Energy	175 Kcals/730 kJ
Fat, total	6.81 g
Saturated fat	2.31 g
Cholesterol	66.37 mg

COOK'S TIP: It is important to choose lean, tender meat for stir-fries like this, as it is cooked in the minimum of time.

Jamaican Black Bean Pot

Molasses imparts a rich, treacly flavour to the spicy sauce, which incorporates a stunning mix of black beans, vibrant red and yellow (bell) peppers and orange butternut squash.

Serves 4

INGREDIENTS
225 g/8 oz/1¼ cups dried black beans
1 bay leaf
15 ml/1 tbsp vegetable oil
1 large onion, chopped
1 garlic clove, chopped
5 ml/1 tsp English mustard powder
15 ml/1 tbsp blackstrap molasses
30 ml/2 tbsp soft dark brown sugar
5 ml/1 tsp dried thyme
2.5 ml/½ tsp dried chilli flakes
5 ml/1 tsp vegetable bouillon powder
1 red (bell) pepper, seeded and diced
1 yellow (bell) pepper, seeded and diced
450 g/1 lb/5¼ cups butternut squash or
    pumpkin, seeded and cut into 1 cm/½ in
    dice
salt and freshly ground black pepper
fresh thyme sprigs, to garnish
boiled rice, to serve

1 Soak the beans overnight in plenty of water, then drain and rinse well. Place in a large pan, cover with fresh water and add the bay leaf.

Nutritional Notes	
Energy	283 Kcals/1176 kJ
Fat, total	4.1 g
Saturated fat	0.7 g
Cholesterol	0 mg

2 Bring to the boil, then boil rapidly for 10 minutes. Reduce the heat, cover, and simmer for 30 minutes until tender. Drain, reserving the cooking water. Preheat the oven to 180°C/ 350°F/Gas 4.

3 Heat the oil in a frying pan and sauté the onion and garlic for about 5 minutes until softened, stirring occasionally. Add the mustard powder, molasses, sugar, dried thyme and chilli and cook for 1 minute, stirring. Stir in the black beans, then spoon the mixture into a flameproof casserole.

4 Add enough water to the reserved bean cooking liquid to make 400 ml/ 14 fl oz/1⅔ cups, then mix in the bouillon powder and pour into the casserole. Stir into the beans, then bake in the oven for 25 minutes.

5 Add the peppers and squash or pumpkin and mix well. Cover, then bake for 45 minutes more until the vegetables are tender. Serve garnished with fresh thyme and accompanied by boiled rice.

Braised Barley & Vegetables

One of the oldest of cultivated cereals, pot barley has a nutty flavour and slightly chewy texture. It makes a warming and filling dish when combined with root vegetables.

Serves 4

INGREDIENTS
200 g/7 oz/1 cup pearl or pot barley
15 ml/1 tbsp sunflower oil
1 large onion, chopped
2 celery sticks, sliced
2 carrots, sliced thickly
225 g/8 oz swede (rutabaga) or turnip, cut
    into 2 cm/¾ in cubes
225 g/8 oz potatoes, cut into 2 cm/¾ in cubes
475 ml/16 fl oz/2 cups vegetable stock
salt and freshly ground black pepper
celery leaves, to garnish

1 Put the barley in a measuring jug and add water to reach the 600 ml/ 1 pint/2½ cup mark. Leave to soak in a cool place for at least 4 hours or, preferably, overnight.

2 Heat the oil in a large pan and fry the onion for 5 minutes. Add the celery and carrots and cook for 3–4 minutes or until the onion is starting to brown.

3 Add the barley and its soaking liquid to the pan. Then add the swede or turnip, potatoes and stock. Season with salt and pepper. Bring to the boil, reduce the heat and cover the pan.

4 Simmer for 40 minutes or until most of the stock has been absorbed and the barley is tender. Stir occasionally towards the end of cooking to prevent the barley from sticking to the base of the pan. Serve garnished with celery leaves.

Nutritional Notes	
Energy	297 Kcals/1235 kJ
Fat, total	4.2 g
Saturated fat	0.4 g
Cholesterol	0 mg

Balti Potatoes with Aubergines

A heavenly mixture of Balti spices enhances this low-calorie dish.

Serves 4

INGREDIENTS
10–12 baby potatoes
6 small aubergines (eggplant)
1 medium red (bell) pepper
15 ml/1 tbsp corn oil
2 medium onions, sliced
4–6 curry leaves
2.5 ml/½ tsp onion seeds
5 ml/1 tsp crushed coriander seeds
2.5 ml/½ tsp cumin seeds
5 ml/1 tsp finely chopped fresh root ginger
5 ml/1 tsp crushed garlic
5 ml/1 tsp crushed dried red chillies
15 ml/1 tbsp chopped fresh fenugreek
5 ml/1 tsp chopped fresh coriander (cilantro),
    plus whole leaves to garnish
15 ml/1 tbsp plain low-fat yogurt

1 Cook the unpeeled potatoes in boiling water until just soft. Set aside. Cut the aubergines into quarters. Cut the red pepper in half, discard the seeds, then slice the flesh into strips.

2 Heat the oil in a non-stick wok and fry the onions, curry leaves, onion seeds, crushed coriander seeds and cumin seeds for 5 minutes or until the onions are a soft golden brown.

3 Add the ginger, garlic, chillies and fenugreek, followed by the pepper, aubergines and potatoes. Stir everything together and cover with a lid. Lower the heat and cook for 5–7 minutes.

4 Remove the lid, add the chopped coriander followed by the yogurt, and stir well. Serve garnished with whole coriander leaves.

Nutritional Notes	
Energy	150 Kcals/624 kJ
Fat, total	3.6 g
Saturated fat	0.6 g
Cholesterol	0.2 mg

COOK'S TIP: To prevent curdling, it is always best to whisk yogurt before adding it to a hot dish.

Red Cabbage & Apple Casserole

The brilliant colour and pungent flavour make this an excellent winter dish.

Serves 6

INGREDIENTS
3 onions, chopped
2 fennel bulbs, roughly chopped
675 g/1½ lb red cabbage, shredded
30 ml/2 tbsp caraway seeds
3 tart eating apples or 1 large cooking apple
300 ml/½ pint/1¼ cups plain low-fat yogurt
15 ml/1 tbsp creamed horseradish sauce
salt and freshly ground black pepper

Nutritional Notes	
Energy	98 Kcals/407 kJ
Fat, total	1.2 g
Saturated fat	0.3 g
Cholesterol	18 mg

1 Preheat the oven to 150°C/300°F/ Gas 2. Mix the onions, fennel, cabbage and caraway seeds in a bowl. Peel and chop the apples, then stir them into the cabbage mixture.

2 Transfer to a casserole. Mix the yogurt with the creamed horseradish sauce and stir into the casserole.

3 Season with salt and pepper and cover tightly. Bake for 1½ hours, stirring once or twice. Serve hot.

COOK'S TIP: This casserole can be served with plain boiled rice. Include this in your calorie count.

Vegetable Casserole

Serves 4

INGREDIENTS
15 ml/1 tbsp olive oil
675 g/1½ lb frozen broad (fava) beans
4 turnips, sliced
4 leeks, sliced
1 red (bell) pepper, seeded and sliced
200 g/7 oz fresh spinach leaves or 115 g/4 oz
    frozen spinach
2 x 400 g/14 oz cans artichoke hearts, drained
30 ml/2 tbsp pumpkin seeds
soy sauce
salt and freshly ground black pepper
rice, baked jacket potatoes or wholemeal
    (whole-wheat) bread, to serve (optional)

1 Preheat the oven to 180°C/350°F/
Gas 4. Brush a casserole with the oil.

2 Cook the broad beans in a
saucepan of boiling, lightly salted water
for about 10 minutes. Drain and place
with the next five ingredients in the
casserole. Cover the casserole and bake
in the oven for 30–40 minutes or until
the turnips are soft.

3 Stir in the pumpkin seeds and soy
sauce to taste. Season with pepper.
Serve alone or with rice, baked jacket
potatoes or bread, if you prefer.

Nutritional Notes	
Energy	258 Kcals/1074 kJ
Fat, total	9.0 g
Saturated fat	1.3 g
Cholesterol	0 mg

Fettuccine with Broccoli & Garlic

Just add a mixed salad to make this a complete and delicious main course.

Serves 4

INGREDIENTS

3–4 garlic cloves, crushed
350 g/12 oz/3 cups broccoli florets
150 ml/¼ pint/⅔ cup vegetable stock
60 ml/4 tbsp white wine
30 ml/2 tbsp chopped fresh basil
60 ml/4 tbsp grated Parmesan cheese
350 g/12 oz/3 cups fettuccine or tagliatelle
salt and freshly ground black pepper
fresh basil leaves, to garnish
mixed leaf salad, to serve

1 Cook the garlic and broccoli in the stock for 5 minutes until tender. Mash roughly with a fork or potato masher. Add the wine, basil and Parmesan cheese. Season to taste.

2 Cook the fettuccine or tagliatelle in a large pan of boiling, salted water according to the packet instructions until *al dente*. Drain thoroughly.

3 Return the pasta to the pan with half the broccoli sauce, toss to coat, then transfer to serving plates. Top with the remaining broccoli sauce, garnish with basil leaves and serve with salad.

Nutritional Notes	
Energy	411 Kcals/1709 kJ
Fat, total	7.3 g
Saturated fat	3.5 g
Cholesterol	15 mg

Risotto Primavera

A substantial one-pot vegetarian main dish that is low in calories.

Serves 4

INGREDIENTS
10 ml/2 tsp olive oil
1 medium onion, sliced
250 g/9 oz/1¼ cups short grain rice
2.5 ml/½ tsp ground turmeric
600 ml/1 pint/2½ cups vegetable stock
250 g/9 oz mixed spring vegetables, left
   whole if small
45 ml/3 tbsp chopped fresh parsley
salt and freshly ground black pepper
30 ml/2 tbsp grated Parmesan cheese
   (optional), to serve

1 Heat the oil in a non-stick pan and fry the onion until golden. Stir in the rice and cook for 1–2 minutes.

2 Add the turmeric, vegetable stock and seasoning. Bring to the boil, then add the vegetables.

3 Return to the boil, cover the pan and cook gently, stirring occasionally, for 20 minutes or until the rice is tender and most of the liquid has been absorbed. Add more stock if necessary.

4 Stir in the parsley and adjust the seasoning to taste. Serve hot, lightly sprinkled with Parmesan, if using.

Nutritional Notes	
Energy	102 Kcals/424 kJ
Fat, total	0.4 g
Saturated fat	0.04 g
Cholesterol	0 mg

Rice Noodles with Vegetable Chilli Sauce

The vegetables here are red pepper, carrots, baby sweetcorn, bamboo shoots and kidney beans, gently simmered together in a spicy sauce.

Serves 4

INGREDIENTS

15 ml/1 tbsp sunflower oil
1 onion, chopped
2 garlic cloves, crushed
1 fresh red chilli, seeded and finely chopped
1 red (bell) pepper, seeded and diced
1 carrot, finely chopped
175 g/6 oz/1 cup baby sweetcorn, halved
225 g/8 oz can sliced bamboo shoots, rinsed and drained
200 g/7 oz can red kidney beans, rinsed and drained
300 ml/½ pint/1¼ cups passata or sieved tomatoes
15 ml/1 tbsp soy sauce
5 ml/1 tsp ground coriander
175 g/6 oz rice noodles
30 ml/2 tbsp chopped fresh coriander (cilantro) or parsley
salt and freshly ground black pepper
fresh parsley sprigs, to garnish

1 Heat the oil, add the onion, garlic, chilli and red pepper and cook for 5 minutes, stirring. Stir in the carrot, sweetcorn, bamboo shoots, kidney beans, passata or sieved tomatoes, soy sauce and ground coriander.

2 Bring to the boil, then cover, reduce the heat and simmer gently for 30 minutes, or until the vegetables are tender, stirring occasionally. Season with salt and pepper to taste.

3 Meanwhile, place the noodles in a bowl and cover with boiling water. Stir with a fork and leave to stand for 3–4 minutes or according to the packet instructions. Rinse with boiling water and drain thoroughly.

Nutritional Notes	
Energy	274 Kcals/1140 kJ
Fat, total	3.8 g
Saturated fat	0.4 g
Cholesterol	0 mg

COOK'S TIP: After handling chillies, wash your hands, as the oils can burn your eyes, if touched.

4 Stir the fresh coriander or parsley into the sauce. Spoon the noodles on to warmed serving plates and top with the sauce. Garnish with parsley sprigs and serve.

Poached Pears in Maple-yogurt Sauce

An elegant dessert, ideal for low-calorie entertaining, that is easier to make than it looks – poach the pears in advance, and have the cooled syrup ready to spoon on to the plates just before serving.

Serves 6

INGREDIENTS
6 firm dessert pears
15 ml/1 tbsp lemon juice
250 ml/8 fl oz/1 cup sweet white wine or cider
thinly pared rind of 1 lemon
1 cinnamon stick
30 ml/2 tbsp maple syrup
2.5 ml/½ tsp arrowroot
150 g/5 oz/⅔ cup low-fat Greek-style (strained, low-fat) yogurt

1 Thinly peel the pears, leaving them whole and with stalks intact. Brush them with lemon juice to prevent them from browning. Scoop out the core from the base of each pear.

2 Place the pears in a wide, heavy-based pan and pour over the wine or cider, with enough cold water almost to cover the pears.

3 Add the lemon rind and cinnamon stick, then bring to the boil. Reduce the heat, cover the pan and simmer the pears gently for 30–40 minutes or until just tender. Turn the pears occasionally so that they cook evenly. Lift out the pears carefully, draining them well.

4 Bring the liquid to the boil and boil, uncovered, to reduce to about 120 ml/4 fl oz/½ cup. Strain and add the maple syrup. Blend a little of the liquid with the arrowroot. Return to the pan and cook, stirring, until thick and clear. Cool.

5 Slice each pear about three-quarters of the way through, leaving the slices attached at the stem end. Fan out each pear on a serving plate.

6 Stir 30 ml/2 tbsp of the cooled pear syrup into the yogurt and spoon it around the fanned pears. Serve immediately.

Nutritional Notes	
Energy	173 Kcals/719 kJ
Fat, total	0.31 g
Saturated fat	0.2 g
Cholesterol	1.5 mg

Cinnamon & Apricot Soufflés

Don't expect this to be difficult simply because it is a soufflé – it really could not be easier and, best of all, it is very low in calories.

Serves 4

INGREDIENTS
a little low-fat spread, for greasing
a little plain (all-purpose) flour, for dusting
3 eggs
115 g/4 oz/scant ½ cup apricot fruit spread
finely grated rind of ½ lemon
5 ml/1 tsp ground cinnamon,
 plus extra to decorate

1 Preheat the oven to 190°C/375°F/ Gas 5. Grease four individual soufflé dishes and dust them with flour.

COOK'S TIP: Puréed fresh or well-drained canned fruit can be used instead of the apricot spread, but make sure the mixture is not too wet or the soufflé will not rise properly. Adjust your calorie count accordingly.

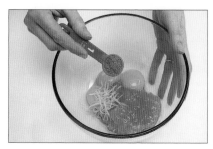

2 Separate the eggs and place the yolks in a bowl with the apricot fruit spread, lemon rind and cinnamon. Whisk hard until the mixture is thick and pale in colour.

3 Place the egg whites in a clean bowl and whisk them until they are stiff enough to hold soft peaks.

4 Using a metal spoon or spatula, fold the beaten egg whites evenly into the yolk mixture.

5 Divide the soufflé mixture among the prepared dishes and bake for 10–15 minutes until well-risen and golden brown. Serve the soufflés immediately, dusted with a little extra ground cinnamon.

Nutritional Notes	
Energy	98 Kcals/407 kJ
Fat, total	4.6 g
Saturated fat	1.3 g
Cholesterol	164.5 mg

55

Strawberry Gâteau

It is hard to believe that this delicious gâteau is low in calories, but it is true, so enjoy! Ring the changes with other soft fruits, if you like.

Serves 6

INGREDIENTS
2 eggs
75 g/3 oz/6 tbsp caster (superfine) sugar
grated rind of ½ orange
50 g/2 oz/½ cup plain (all-purpose) flour
strawberry leaves, to decorate (optional)
icing sugar, for dusting

FOR THE FILLING
275 g/10 oz/1¼ cups low-fat soft cheese
grated rind of ½ orange
30 ml/2 tbsp caster (superfine) sugar
60 ml/4 tbsp low-fat fromage frais
225 g/8 oz/2 cups strawberries, halved
25 g/1 oz/¼ cup chopped almonds, toasted

1 Preheat the oven to 190°C/375°F/ Gas 5. Grease a 30 x 20 cm/12 x 8 in Swiss roll tin and line with non-stick baking paper.

2 In a bowl, whisk the eggs, sugar and orange rind together until thick and mousse-like.

3 Fold in the flour. Turn into the prepared tin. Bake for 15–20 minutes or until the cake springs back when lightly pressed. Turn out on to a wire rack, remove the paper and leave to cool.

4 Meanwhile, to make the filling, mix the soft cheese with the orange rind, sugar and fromage frais. Divide between two bowls. Chop half the strawberry halves and add to one bowl of filling.

5 Cut the sponge widthways into three equal pieces and sandwich them together with the strawberry filling. Spread two-thirds of the plain filling over the sides of the cake and press on the toasted almonds.

Nutritional Notes	
Energy	151 Kcals/628 kJ
Fat, total	4.5 g
Saturated fat	0.8 g
Cholesterol	73.7 mg

6 Spread the rest of the filling over the top of the cake and decorate with the remaining strawberry halves, and strawberry leaves, if liked. Dust with icing sugar and serve.

Mango & Amaretti Strudel

Fresh mango and crushed amaretti wrapped in wafer-thin filo pastry make a special treat that is high in scrumptiousness but low in calories.

Serves 4

INGREDIENTS
1 large mango
grated rind of 1 lemon
2 amaretti biscuits
25 g/1 oz/2 tbsp demerara sugar
15 g/½ oz/3 tbsp wholemeal (whole-wheat) breadcrumbs
2 sheets filo pastry, each 48 x 28 cm/19 x 11 in, defrosted if frozen
10 g/½ tbsp low-fat soft margarine, melted
10 g/¼ oz/1 tbsp chopped almonds
icing (confectioner's) sugar, for dusting

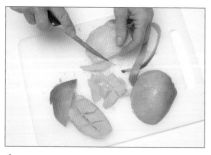

1 Preheat the oven to 190°C/375°FGas 5. Lightly grease a large baking sheet. Cut the mango on each side of the stone. Peel, and cut the flesh into cubes, then place them in a bowl and sprinkle with the grated lemon rind.

2 Crush the amaretti biscuits and mix them with the demerara sugar and the wholemeal breadcrumbs.

3 Lay one sheet of filo on a flat surface and brush with a quarter of the melted margarine. Top with the second sheet, brush with one-third of the remaining margarine, then fold both sheets over to make a rectangle measuring 28 x 24 cm/11 x 9½ in. Brush with half the remaining margarine.

4 Sprinkle the filo with the amaretti mixture, leaving a 5 cm/2 in border on each long side. Arrange the mango cubes over the top.

5 Roll up the filo from one of the long sides. Lift the strudel on to the baking sheet with the join underneath. Brush with the remaining margarine and sprinkle with almonds.

Nutritional Notes	
Energy	188 Kcals/781 kJ
Fat, total	3.8 g
Saturated fat	0.6 g
Cholesterol	1.7 mg

6 Bake for 20–25 minutes until golden brown, then transfer to a board. Dust with the icing sugar, slice diagonally and serve warm.

COOK'S TIP: During preparation, cover unused filo with a damp dish towel to prevent it from drying.

Baked Blackberry Cheesecake

This light, low-calorie cheesecake is best made with wild blackberries, if available, though cultivated ones will produce a good result.

Serves 5

INGREDIENTS

175 g/6 oz/¾ cup cottage cheese
150 g/5 oz/⅔ cup plain low-fat yogurt
15 ml/1 tbsp plain wholemeal (whole-wheat) flour
25 g/1 oz/2 tbsp golden caster (superfine) sugar
1 egg
1 egg white
finely grated rind and juice of ½ lemon
200 g/7 oz/2 cups fresh or frozen blackberries, thawed

1 Preheat the oven to 180°C/350°F/ Gas 4. Lightly grease and base-line an 18 cm/7 in sandwich tin (pan).

2 Place the cottage cheese in a food processor and process until smooth. Alternatively, rub it through a sieve to achieve a smooth texture.

3 Place the cottage cheese in a bowl, add the low-fat yogurt, wholemeal flour, caster sugar, egg and egg white, and mix thoroughly. Add the lemon rind and juice and blackberries, reserving a few for decoration.

4 Tip the cheesecake mixture into the prepared sandwich tin and bake for 30–35 minutes, or until just set. Turn off the oven and leave for a further 30 minutes.

5 Run a knife around the edge of the cheesecake to loosen it from the tin, and carefully turn it out. Remove the lining paper.

6 Place the cheesecake on a warm serving plate. Decorate with the reserved blackberries and serve warm.

Nutritional Notes	
Energy	100 Kcals/416 kJ
Fat, total	2.11 g
Saturated fat	0.8 g
Cholesterol	46.8 mg

Apple & Banana Crumble

A fabulous, low-calorie version of an old favourite, with a natural sweetness.

Serves 6

INGREDIENTS

2 large cooking apples, cored and chopped
2 large bananas, peeled and sliced
60 ml/4 tbsp water
25 g/1 oz/2 tbsp low-fat spread
30–45 ml/2–3 tbsp pear and apple spread
25 g/1 oz/¼ cup wholemeal (whole-wheat) flour
75 g/3 oz/¾ cup porridge oats
15 ml/1 tbsp sunflower seeds
low-fat yogurt, to serve (optional)

1 Preheat the oven to 180°C/350°F/ Gas 4. Mix the apples, bananas and water in a pan and cook until soft and pulpy.

2 Melt the low-fat spread with the pear and apple spread in a separate pan. Stir in the flour, oats and sunflower seeds, and mix well.

3 Transfer the apple and banana mixture to an 18 cm/7 in baking dish and spread the oat crumble over the top. Bake for about 20 minutes or until the topping is golden brown. Serve warm or at room temperature, alone or with low-fat yogurt, if liked.

Nutritional Notes	
Energy	176 Kcals/733 kJ
Fat, total	4.3 g
Saturated fat	0.8 g
Cholesterol	0.3 mg

Banana & Pineapple Ice Cream

Half the cream is substituted with low-calorie yogurt for a superb ice cream.

Serves 4

INGREDIENTS
1 banana
150 g/5 oz fresh pineapple
150 ml/¼ pint/⅔ cup plain low-fat yogurt
150 ml/¼ pint/⅔ cup whipping cream, lightly
   whipped
fresh mint sprig, to decorate

1 Purée the banana and pineapple in a blender or food processor. Tip the purée into a large bowl and stir in the yogurt. Fold in the cream.

COOK'S TIP: Drained canned pineapple in fruit juice can be substituted for the fresh pineapple.

2 Churn the mixture in an ice-cream maker. Alternatively, place it in a suitable container for freezing. Freeze for about 2 hours until ice crystals form around the edges. Process or beat the mixture until it is smooth, then return it to the freezer.

3 Repeat the process once or twice, then freeze until firm. Remove from the freezer to soften slightly before serving, decorated with mint.

Nutritional Notes	
Energy	200 Kcals/832 kJ
Fat, total	15.2 g
Saturated fat	9.5 g
Cholesterol	0 mg

This edition is published by Lorenz Books,
an imprint of Anness Publishing Ltd,
Blaby Road, Wigston, LE18 4SE

www.lorenzbooks.com; www.annesspublishing.com

If you like the images in this book and would like to investigate
using them for publishing, promotions or advertising, please visit
our website www.practicalpictures.com for more information.

Publisher: Joanna Lorenz
Editor: Valerie Ferguson & Helen Sudell
Series Designer: Bobbie Colgate Stone
Designer: Andrew Heath
Production Controller: Steve Lang
Recipes contributed by: Catherine Atkinson, Michelle Berriedale-
Johnson, Kathy Brown, Trish Davies, Patrizia Diemling, Christine
France, Silvano Franco, Nicola Graimes, Carole Handslip, Deh-Ta
Hsuing, Shedzad Husain, Lesley Mackley, Sue Maggs, Kathy Man,
Sallie Morris, Maggie Pannell, Anne Sheasby, Jeni Wright.
Photography: William Adams-Lingwood,
Karl Adamson, Mickie Dowie, James Duncan,
Ian Garlick, Michelle Garrett, Amanda Heywood, Ferguson Hill,
Janine Hosegood, David Jordan, Don Last, Patrick McLeavey,
Thomas Odulate, Peter Reilly.

A CIP catalogue record for this book is available from
the British Library

COOK'S NOTES

Bracketed terms are intended for American readers.
For all recipes, quantities are given in both metric and imperial
measures and, where appropriate, in standard cups and spoons.
Follow one set of measures, but not a mixture, because they are
not interchangeable.

Standard spoon and cup measures are level. 1 tsp = 5ml, 1 tbsp =
15ml, 1 cup = 250ml/8fl oz. Australian standard tablespoons are
20ml. Australian readers should use 3 tsp
in place of 1 tbsp for measuring small quantities.

American pints are 16fl oz/2 cups. American readers should use
20fl oz/2.5 cups in place of 1 pint when measuring liquids.

Electric oven temperatures in this book are for conventional
ovens. When using a fan oven, the temperature will probably need
to be reduced by about 10–20°C/20–40°F. Since ovens vary, you
should check with your manufacturer's instruction book for
guidance.

Medium (US large) eggs are used unless otherwise stated.

PUBLISHER'S NOTE: